A Cup of Tears

BY FLORENCE SMITH
&
BONNIE KAY WORLEY

A Cup of Tears

By Florence Smith & Bonnie Kay Worley

ISBN 0-912299-94-0

Library of Congress Control Number: 00-131498

Published in the United States of America

STONEYDALE PRESS PUBLISHING COMPANY
523 Main Street • Stevensville, Montana 59879
Phone: 406-777-2729

DEDICATION

To MARIE,

in her memory and to her family for their assistance in the telling of this story.

Acknowledgments

The authors make the following special acknowledgments in regard to the long time and work involved in the preparation of this book:

Florence Smith:

•My family.

•Marie Johnson's family:

Gene and Chester Johnson
Lillian Stephenson
Helen McClellan
Gloria Eddy

Bonnie Worley:

•My husband, Jerry

•My family

•Stoney Hardcastle, my creative writing teacher, who encouraged me to write

•JoEllen Provence, who proofread the manuscript

PROLOGUE

Russia, or as it was called since 1917, the Union of Soviet Socialist Republics, consisted of over eight and one-half million square miles, one-sixth of the earth's land surface. It encompassed eleven time zones and spanned two continents – Europe and Asia. The Ural Mountains provided the "Great Wall of Europe" that separated Western Russia from Eastern Russia, or Siberia.

Actually, the division of the country by the Urals was more a state of mind than actual elevation. The Urals were not that high, but they extended from islands in the Arctic Ocean almost to the Caspian Sea, a distance of nearly 2,000 miles. European Russia had absorbed many of the aspects of the Industrial Revolution; Asian Russia was almost as primitive as the Western Russians believed it to be.

Czar Alexander freed the serfs in Russia in 1861. The peasants were now allowed to own the land they had worked as serfs. However, land distribution was extremely slow. Allotments were too small for survival and redemption payments too high. Peasants were still hampered by backward methods of cultivation and lack of capital. The previous owners did not know how to farm and the newly freed serfs had no money to farm. There was simply not sufficient land in European Russia for all to survive.

As an incentive to anyone who was willing to move east across the Ural Mountains, the government granted tools and animals. Many who took advantage of this offer had never known serfdom, but had been exploited by traders and usurers. There were a few small religious groups who seized this opportunity for freedom of worship. Land hunger became the prime motivation for the movement to the unknown east.

Since 1540 political prisoners had been banished to Siberia. The more severe the crime, the further east the exile was forced to go. This not only solved political problems but helped develop and populate an empty country. Exiles were generally not proficient in farming and made poor settlers. They made no attempt to learn the languages of the many ethnic groups, nor tried to fit into their varied cultures and lifestyles. Many. fairly well educated, brought their own diverse skills and customs which were unacceptable to the fiercely independent natives, many who were descendants of early Mongols. This "Golden Horde" had swept through Siberia and left a trail of total devastation reaching as far west as Hungary, past the Urals almost to Moscow, in the thirteenth century.

The Mongols were not the first to claim much of Russia. In the ninth century, Swedish Norsemen conquered the native Slavic peoples, founded a Russian state, and fostered trade, especially with Constantinople. Constantinople was not only a trading center, but also the center of the Greek Orthodox Christian Religion. When the city fell to the turks in 1453, the head of the Eastern Orthodox Church was moved to Moscow.

Mongol control of the region was broken when Ivan III refused to pay them tribute. He was aided by the fiercely independent Cossacks, feared and fearless warriors who planted, hunted, trapped and raised horses in the valleys of the Don and Dneiper Rivers.

The ensuing "period of turmoil" resulted in the establishment of the Romanov dynasty which was to last for over 300 years from 1613 to 1917.

Meantime, emigration from border countries was providing a mixture of nationalities with only one thing in common, the tax they all had to pay. The Mongols had instigated the yasak, which was a tax or contribution of one-tenth of all furs harvested. The Cossacks continued the levy as furs were the one product desired by Russia and the rest of the trading world. Forts were established throughout Siberia where the tax was collected. Russians were exempt from taxes. Anyone could become Russian simply by professing the Orthodoxy of the Russian Church. Thus "Russian" no longer denoted a particular nationality, but a "believer."

There were Tatars, a name given by the Chinese to all Mongols, but Tatars were originally of Turkish descent; Ukranians of Polish descent; Buryats, who were Buddhist Mongols; Yakuts of Turkish stock; and many others who spoke their own dialects and asked only to be left alone.

Siberia was of no great significance to West Russia until 1858 when it became a source of furs so prized by the aristocracy and nobility, as well as a rich source of trade to neighboring countries, especially China which felt totally removed from the Russian "Barbarians." The Chinese nobility adopted the sable and otter furs as status symbols and the Russians wanted the tea they were unable to grow for themselves.

While fur traders had the Czar's permission to encroach on native hunting grounds, and were, in fact, encouraged to convert natives to Russian ways, they were never to sell alcohol to the them. Unfortunately, they did not obey and the administration was too corrupt to care. In eastern Siberia, fur trade was flourishing. So long as the furs kept coming, there was no concern for the welfare of those so far removed from governmental influence.

By 1900 the vast majority of Siberians were rural peasants; less than ten per cent lived in urban areas. Peasants were oppressed by the wealthy who controlled trade and exacted tithes through the village chief who allotted the land.

The land was not kind to settlers – it was difficult to clear, swampy, and the soil was poor for the most part. The weather was uncooperative – the only sure weather prediction was that "snow would come early and stay late."

The peasants were barely aware that in the far distance was a Czar. They had no knowledge of the vast fortunes spent on works of art, jewelry, palaces ornately decorated in gold and semi-precious stones, and the expansive, expensive favors at court. They cared little about anything except survival on their allotted acreage using the crude tools they could make or manage to buy. Small villages were almost totally self-sufficient.

Such was the setting when Marie Zimina was born on January 4, 1899, to Epistina Zimina and Ivan Zimin. (In Russia, feminine last names always end in "A".)

CHAPTER ONE

A CUP OF TEARS

With mixed feelings Marie Johnson leaned against the rail of the U.S. Coast Guard cutter BEAR as she gazed across the ice pack at the receding Siberian coastline of Koluchin Bay. She could hardly make out the outline of the driftwood and walrus skin hut that had been her home for almost three years. Built on the ever-frozen tundra, the hut had sheltered them from temperatures plunging to -70 degrees below zero and blowing winds that could exceed 70 miles per hour.

Marie shivered as the cold September Arctic wind swept across the deck, flapping the sails of the cutter. Clutching the rail with one hand, she steadied herself against the pitching and rolling boat as it tossed about on the angry sea. With the other hand, she hugged her 14-month old baby boy, Chester, to her breast. Her sealskin and reindeer parka shielded them both, except for her face. The wolverine ruff on her hood only partially blocked the icy wind as it stung her cheeks and brought tears to her blue eyes.

Carl, her husband, stood silently beside them staring stonily at the disappearing shoreline. He had wanted to stay. But she had insisted on escaping. She was so relieved to be leaving the frozen, barren, isolated trading post that was now under Communist control. She was tired of being cold and hungry and the only white woman in the area. Her few Eskimo and English words could not express her emotions to her Swedish-born American husband, who understood very little of her native Russian language and even less of her totally different beliefs and lifestyle.

Now, in 1923, having been rescued from the clutches of the Communists, with trepidation mixed with excitement, she wondered what awaited them in the future in the United States of America. Communicating with her husband had been difficult because of the language barrier; how could she communicate with others in America with the few English words she had learned?

Chester began to cry, distracting her from her muddled thoughts. To quiet him, and to ease her own apprehension, she began to sing. The creaking, clanking and swaying of the cutter's rigging provided strange accompaniment. The old Russian lullaby brought tears to her eyes. A deep sadness enveloped her. Images of her mother singing that same song reminded her of her family in Antipina whom she had not seen for four years.

Singing had always had a calming effect on Marie when under stress. It lifted her spirits as her clear soprano voice rang out at birthdays, holidays, church, school, even the political rallies for Lenin and Trotsky. Looking back, she wondered if she would have sung so happily for Lenin and Trotsky had she known that the turmoil and the impact of the Communist Revolution would so dramatically change her life and precipitate the chaotic chain of events that had led her to the deck of the BEAR.

All she had ever wanted to do was earn enough money to go home to be with her family in western Siberia. Now, as a gust of wind swirled and snapped the sails taut, she was being carried farther and farther away, her life blown along by circumstances – like a dandelion seed buffeted and caught up in a windstorm, not knowing where she would come to rest and put down new roots.

Staggering as the cutter plunged into another wave, Marie gripped Chester more tightly. Salty ocean spray washed over the bow when the cutter wheeled to starboard. Fighting to keep her footing upon the heaving deck, she made her way to the steps leading to their assigned bunks below. Carl followed carrying the last of their possessions they had hurriedly packed. The stuffy cabin air smelled of the many unwashed, sweaty bodies forced to share the cramped quarters.

Hurling the bags to the floor without speaking, Carl turned and left. She realized that he was still angry at her for insisting they leave the Koluchin Bay fur trading post before he had collected the three years' wages due him from the Phoenix Northern Arctic Fur Trading Company. The ultimatum she had given him not many hours ago was still fresh in her mind.

"You can stay, but I am going. I am taking Chester with me," she defiantly told him.

The crew of the BEAR had hailed them off-shore to ask if they wanted to be evacuated to the United States. By now the Communists had seized control of all Siberia after months of conflict with the White

Russians. They had confiscated all supplies and furs at the trading post and coldly informed them, "Your properties are under arrest. You are now working for the Communist government."

Marie's legs felt like rubber. She had tried to adjust to the up and down movement of the lunging cutter as it struggled against the wind-swept waves. Her queasy stomach was trying to adjust to the erratic movement. Placing her baby on a bunk, she lay down beside him, comforting him. Somehow the motion seemed less terrifying lying on the narrow bunk. Uncoiling her long braids of chestnut brown hair, she laid her head on the damp moldy-smelling pillow.

Chester quickly fell asleep. As he slept, a kaleidoscope of images of her family, her home, and life in her village of Antipina flooded her thoughts. How had she gotten herself into this situation? Four years ago when she told her sister she would travel east to Vladivostok to purchase supplies for Barbara's shop, she never imagined in her wildest dreams that she wouldn't be able to go back home to the small village where she was born. It seemed like a different lifetime. A single tear trickled down her cheek as images of home flashed through her mind.

Antipina was located on a flat plain halfway between Tobolsk and Tyumen, Siberia, a distance of 120 miles. The small community, seven miles from Marie's home, boasted of a one-room Russian Orthodox Church with a single dome and cross, one small trading shop and about one hundred homes.

The Ural Mountains looming just to the west and running north and south for hundreds of miles, provided a wall separating European Russia and Asian Russia that was much wider apart than mere distance. The two regions were as different geographically, economically, culturally, and politically as night is to day. Marie liked to view the mountains in the distance, but gave no time or thought to what lay to the west.

She had always wanted to travel, but this was not quite what she had in mind. When she left Antipina and traveled 4,400 miles on the Trans-Siberian Railroad to Vladivostok, she had planned to be gone for only two weeks. Never, never, would she have believed that she would not be able to go back home. How could she have known that the scheduled five-day train trip would take 16 days, that the Communists would close off the railroad, leaving her stranded in a strange city with very little money, that she would be dodging bullets from the Japanese, and that she would go looking for gold in Kamchatka – just to earn money to go home?

That first winter in the Arctic she had almost starved to death before she met and married forty-five year-old Carl who operated the Koluchin Bay trading post. An Eskimo boy who had attended a Russian school translated their marriage vows on the boat four miles out at sea where a ship's captain performed the ceremony.

Marie lay there thinking, "So many things have happened since I left to go on that fateful shopping trip. Swept up in an avalanche of events, struggling to stay alive, I have had to learn to survive loneliness, starvation, frostbite, childbirth without help, and the harshest climate in Siberia. Carl assured me that the United States is different. I hope he's right."

CHAPTER TWO

MEMORIES OF PAPA

Marie was exhausted but too keyed up to sleep.

Loneliness overwhelmed her. A deep sadness enveloped her, chilling her to the bone like heavy Arctic fog. Four years had elapsed since she had seen any of her family. Marie thought longingly of her beloved father, Ivan Zamin. How she wished that he could see his grandson, Chester. Papa always worked so hard to support his wife and six children. He became a trader because the limited acreage allocated to the oldest men in the family by the village chief could not maintain his family as he had wanted.

During the nine winter months of the year, she had seldom seen him. He traveled from village to village with horse and sleigh collecting, trading, and selling such items as bark mats, bark ropes, frozen fish and other meats, jams, handiwork or any product people might need or wanted to trade. As many people never left their farms, they were always glad to see him. Papa was a good provider and always made a profit from his business transactions. If he could not sell to his gain, he stored his goods till the price went up. If only he had been able to stay home more with the family. Papa had always told her that if they had more land, he wouldn't have to travel so much.

Marie closed her eyes and pictured her father. He was a handsome man. Though only of medium height, his broad shoulders had always been a haven. She smiled a little as she remembered his mustache tickling her when he kissed her. His sharp blue eyes missed nothing. Papa was an educated man, possibly the illegitimate son of one of the many exiles who were too intelligent and verbal to be permitted to exist in Western Russia. There were many political refugees who felt far enough removed from court to live in comparative safety and comfort in Tyumen. Marie knew nothing of Papa's father. She had heard people say that he had no father and referred to him as "The Bastard", but she was sure no one ever said it to his face.

Papa's mother had died when Marie was just three years old. She was too young to understand grief, but it was exciting to see all the company at the house and the extravagant array of food that was set up in the kitchen. Her grandmother was laid out in her best clothes in the living room before the funeral. Marie shuddered as she remembered how her excitement had turned to fear when she heard the booming voice of

The only picture of Marie as a child in Russia still in existence shows her with her family. She is the child in the bottom front. Others in photo are her sisters Ann and Barbara, at the top from left, and her father Ivan, sister Liz, and mother Epistina, in the center row.

the long-bearded Reader who came from the village to conduct the service. As his thundering voice read from the Bible, she had cowered in the farthest corner of the room. No one seemed to notice her, and she had stayed scared the rest of the day.

Another frightening recollection drifted into her thoughts as she looked around the BEAR's cramped cabin. When she was almost six years old, she became extremely ill. No home remedies had brought any relief. There was no doctor in the village. In her feverish state, drifting in and out of consciousness, she heard her mother crying and her father praying to the icon, an ornately decorated picture of Christ, which hung on the wall. Papa had made a promise to God if he would let her live, but Marie never knew what the promise was.

Afraid she might die, her parents decided she must see a priest. The priest came to Antipina only once a year to hear confessions and collect tithes. Marie would have to be taken to the nearest priest who was at Tobolsk, nearly sixty miles away. Caring people from the village offered to go along to take the icon and Marie. She was bundled up in wool blankets and placed in one of the sleighs. She couldn't remember much about this trip except that the melting snow had left bare ground on the road which caused the runners to drag. The horses strained and snorted as they finally pulled the sled onto a patch of snow which made the sleigh much easier to pull.

Upon reaching the monastery, Marie was aware prayers were being said for her. After two days, she had recovered sufficiently to go home. By this time, there was even less snow, making the return trip much more tedious and hazardous. Recalling how worried her parents had been, and how secure and loved she had felt in her father's arms as he had bundled her up to carry her to the sleigh, she sighed and hugged her sleeping child. How fortunate they were that Chester was healthy, considering there had never been a doctor available at the tip of northeast Siberia.

How she missed her family, especially her father. Summers had been so special. Marie felt so happy working side by side with her father as they toiled in the fields. She was glad that her oldest sister, Barbara, and next-oldest sister, Anna, helped their mother, Epistina, with the multitude of household chores, freeing her to spend summers outside working, riding, and fishing with Papa. Elizabeth was six years younger than Marie but she helped wherever she was able, though her activities were of little interest to Marie.

Her own baby's face clouded her memory when she tried to visualize her baby brother, Peter. Peter had been so young when she left; she scarcely remembered what he looked like. He was ten years younger than she, just an infant when she left home to go to school.

Opening her eyes she gazed down at Chester, asleep on the bunk beside her. She sighed. Her thoughts wandered to her oldest brother, Alexi, who was married and had a family. What would his boys think of their cousin? They were probably too old now to pay much attention, but the girls would likely want to play with him like a doll.

The creaking and groaning of the cutter with its sails filled with wind reminded Marie that she was getting farther and farther away from her family as the boat picked up speed and glided over the waves. Mingled with the loneliness, though, was a sense of deep relief at having escaped the grip of the Communists and the over-powering isolation of the inhospitable Arctic.

Drifting off to sleep, Marie felt a gentle tap on her shoulder as Chester stretched. The twilight between consciousness and sleep invoked a memory.

"Marie, wake up! We must leave early. Today we go to the far field!" Papa said as he gently shook her.

She jumped out of bed anxious to spend time with him. Hurriedly, she began dressing in her homespun garments. Her fingers fumbled as she tried to tie a bow in the drawstring of her voluminous drawers. Quickly donning her coarse linen dress, she slipped her feet into her rubber work boots lined with sheep's wool. Then, gulping down her breakfast of porridge, she scurried to the waiting horses, singing as she went. Oh, how she loved to ride! And riding to the far field would take some time.

When some of the land that belonged to their village was allotted to her father and some to brother Alexi by the village chief, little thought was given to the inconvenience of farming lands that were not adjoining. As the redistribution of land took place every forty years, it would be a long time before another assignment of land would be made. By then baby brother Peter might be able to be included, for only the qualified men could use the land.

"I'm coming, Papa!" she called as she ran.

Trotting down the road astride the harnessed plow horse, Marie smiled to herself because she felt so happy to have Papa all to herself. He was only home the three short months of summer when roads were wet and muddy and nearly impassable. Not till freeze-up in the fall would he be able to resume his trading. Meantime, they would be working and fishing together. They all worked from dawn to dark.

The early morning air was crisp with just a hint of rain. The jangling of the horses' harnesses made a slapping sound against their sides as they trotted down the road. Clouds of vapor from their heavy breathing encircled their bobbing heads. Marie began to sing in time to the clip-clopping hoofbeats. It was a beautiful morning because she was helping Papa.

When they arrived at the field, Marie dismounted. "Marie, today you will harrow by yourself. I am going to finish planting the other field,"

Papa said as he hooked her horses to the double harrows.

Marie felt so excited because she was trusted to work by herself. Proudly guiding the horses, she tried to keep the rows straight like Papa had showed her. All of a sudden, the horses turned too sharply and the harrows became tangled. They were stuck tightly. Marie struggled with the harrows, trying to untangle the metal teeth. She could not pull them loose. She tugged in vain.

"Oh, what will Papa say?" she sobbed as tears began to roll down her cheeks. Papa had trusted her with the harrows and horses, and she had made a mess of things.

To compound her problem, rain began pouring down. She started to shiver in her wet clothing. The horses turned their heads around and looked at her as if to say, "Now, what?"

She struggled on trying to free the harrows. She had wanted to make father proud of her. She was a mess. Her clothes were soaked. She was covered with mud. Utterly miserable, she looked up to see her father coming. She was afraid he would be angry with her. She only had not done the job well, she had made more work for him. Papa had no patience with stupid blunders. He always demanded the best of himself and others.

Dismounting from his horse, he said not a word. He easily lifted the harrow which had been too heavy for her to budge. Papa was so strong. He consoled his weeping daughter, smothering a smile at the appearance of her mud-streaked, tearful face.

Nearby stood an old log cabin. He picked her up and carried her into the deserted building. Starting a fire in the old stove in one corner, he found a kettle and put water on to boil. Into the boiling water he poured a mixture of grains he carried in his knapsack, making a porridge to warm her. His gentle consideration calmed her troubled spirits, and the warmth remained with her all the way home.

Though she had failed at harrowing, she was still happy to have spent that precious time with Papa.

Arriving home, Marie found Mama most unhappy with her. The bath water had to be heated; her filthy clothes had to be washed. And washing clothes was a major project. First, they must fill a big tub on the huge brick stove with water from the river. After the water boiled, the clothes were put in along with homemade, lye soap.

Dreaming, she imagined she could actually smell the combination of lye soap and sweaty woolen clothes as the steam rose from the laundry tub. The hot clothes were transferred with a stick to a basket and then carried to the nearby creek to be rinsed. In the winter, ice had to be cut to provide a hole through which to slosh the boiled garments. Each piece had to be wrung by hand...sometimes freezing even as they were being twisted by numb fingers. In her sleep, Marie's fingers twitched in memory.

Marie was sleeping soundly when the racket from the tapping of a sailor's boot on the deck above her head, along with his lusty tenor as he sang, roused her. The noise was followed by the jangling of chains that reminded her of a tambourine. As she drifted back to sleep, echoing through the cabin came a loud thud from the deck overhead, sounding like a knock on the door.

"Who's there?" called Papa as he opened the door of their one-story log house.

"Do you have any horses to trade today, Mr. Zimin?" asked a dark complexioned, brightly-dressed man at the door as he swooped off his hat.

The Gypsies were back! They came every year and Papa let them camp in his pasture. There would be singing and dancing! How wonderful! If she were careful she could slip away to watch the dancing and listen to the music she dearly loved.

Sometimes Papa would have a horse that could no longer pull his sleigh and the bargaining and drinking would begin. The Gypsies always had horses to sell. They bought the skinny, overworked plugs from the farmers, fattened them, and sold them for much more than they had paid. A bottle of vodka was always thrown in to close a horse-trading deal.

In the meantime, while the men were horse trading, the women went from house to house reading palms and telling fortunes for a little money, a loaf of bread, or anything they could get. Each profitable trade meant a Gypsy celebration around the campfire with singing and dancing accompanied by the playing of instruments.

Marie loved to listen to the accordion. From her secret hiding place she would watch the man with the accordion as he drew it open and closed, while pressing the buttons to make the most beautiful sounds. Two men strummed guitars. The women in their resplendent full skirts whirled around and around with the men dressed in black pants, leather boots, long, embroidered sashes, billowy-sleeved shirts and gaily decorated vests.

Some of the women and children played tambourines as they danced, hitting the drum with the flat of their hands to the rhythm of the accordion music. Bells jingled. The couples swayed to the sound of the fast, lively music. They seemed to be having so much fun. Every so often, one of the laughing, romantic men would sweep his partner off her feet and disappear into one of the wagons.

Marie wanted so much to go down and join them. Papa would be upset if she did! She had been warned about not going near the Gypsies. Rumors abounded that they kidnaped children, but she did not believe that. The Gypsies were too nice to do anything like that. The longer they danced and twirled, the more vodka they all drank. Soon the celebrating slowed down. What fun it was to watch them from her hiding place. They enchanted her.

Marie was always sorry to see them go as they proceeded on their wandering way. They never camped very long in one place. They reminded Marie of the colorful butterflies that land for an instant and then fly away to a new flower or blade of grass. They appeared to Marie to lead such a happy, carefree life, with no fields to plow, or garden to hoe, or crops to harvest. All she ever did was work, and it seemed to her that all they ever did was play.

It would be so much fun to travel all over to new villages and see new sights everyday. They only had to load up their steps, put out their campfire, and they were ready to pursue a new adventure in a new place. She wistfully thought how wonderful that would be as she quietly slipped back to her house.

Other peddlers visited when the frozen ground permitted travel. The most intriguing peddlers were the cat buyers.

“Cats. I'll buy your cats!” rang up and down the street.

Traveling from village to village, from street to street, and from farm to farm, they carried a sleigh filled with pots, pans and other items. Their sleighs were easily recognized for dead cats hung from the top edge.

Every family owned several dogs and cats. The peddler would trade his wares for live cats. A trade completed, the cat peddler grabbed the hissing, spitting cat by the ruff of the neck. Holding it away from his body to avoid the flailing claws, he carried it to his sleigh. Suspended at the top of his sleigh were twenty or more small nooses. Slipping the string over the cat's head, he tightened the loop. He let go of the cat. The weight of the struggling, swinging animal only served to hasten its death. As the cat choked, its eyes bulged out, the mouth gaped open and the tongue flopped out the side of its mouth. This resulted in a perfect hide with no breaks, blemishes, or scars.

The dead cats hung from the pole until they were frozen. The frozen cat carcasses were then stacked like cordwood in the sleigh until all the cat peddler's wares were traded. Then he proceeded to the tanning factory where the cats' hides were sold to make women's coats, coat linings, collars, and gloves. The fur lining was very expensive, as it was strong and long-lasting. The coats were popular among the ladies, for they offered a choice in color of the fur.

Marie shuddered and opened her eyes and realized that the recollection of the horrible sight of the sleigh adorned with the strangled, swaying, stiff cat bodies dangling from their hangman's nooses was just a memory now. And reminiscing and envying the Gypsies for their adventurous lifestyle seemed a lifetime ago.

Gently stroking Chester's hair, she lay there on the bunk in the U.S. Coast Guard cutter, BEAR, unable to sleep as the boat churned on toward the United States of America.

CHAPTER THREE

HOMESICK FOR FAMILY

Fingers of dank glacier-cooled air crept down Marie's neck, inching along her spine. Chester whimpered. In the cramped quarters of the bunk, she changed the moss lining of his diaper. She wished she had proper diapers and clothes for him, like the ones they used in the hospital where she had worked after she was trapped in Vladivostok when the Communists shut off the Trans-Siberian Railroad. Shivering, Marie pulled the Hudson Bay blanket over her head, shutting out the cold air.

Working in the obstetrical ward in the hospital had hardly prepared her for giving birth to her son and delivering him by herself in their trading post at Koluchin Bay, alone, because Carl was on a fur-buying trip. It was a wonder that she and Chester were still alive. Though she questioned whether Carl's presence would have made any difference. He had made it clear he would never wash a cup or help with household chores. She supposed that giving birth came under the category of women's work.

Soon her breath began to warm their cocoon under the blanket. The shaking subsided, but deep inside there was only cold. She felt like she had not been truly warm for years.

She thought longingly of the large brick fireplace at home in Antipina, with the attached baking oven and cooking space. How cozy Papa had made their new home. The old house with its smoke-stained beams and dark interior had been replaced with a bright one-story, many-roomed building when the family had outgrown the old structure. What a difference from the driftwood, sod and walrus skin hut she had called home for almost three years.

Closing her eyes, Marie imagined she was soaking in the tub at home, sensually sliding down into the warm, warm water, heated to just the right temperature on the stove. She could think of only one thing that might compare – that was the pleasure of a community steam bath. Each family in the little community was assigned a specific time to enjoy its use.

Boiling water was poured over cold rocks, producing a cloud of steam that made her sweat and opened her pores. A short brush was used to gently beat the bathers to stimulate circulation. After enjoying the soothing benefits of the steam bath, what a shock when she then jumped into the icy cold water to cool off and close the pores. Oh! How good it felt! Her body became so alive, and her skin had tingled after the refreshing bath. Her home at Koluchin Bay had no such luxuries – and certainly not the BEAR. Reality returned.

Eying the slats of the bunk above her head with distaste, Marie recalled the beautiful birch furniture that Papa built to make their home the finest in the area.

Sharing a room with Elizabeth, her younger sister, had seemed unfair because her two older sisters, Barbara and Anna, each had their own rooms. But now, after all she had been through, she would love to be able to again share a room with Elizabeth.

Laughter and singing echoed throughout the house when they had company. The Zimins were very hospitable, so friends and family visited often. There were wall to wall children sleeping on the floor snuggled under large heavy quilts. There was a special sleeping alcove built in above the kitchen where the warmth from the huge stove kept the sleeper snug and cozy on cold winter nights. Papa had put double glass in the windows for added warmth, but in the winter it was so cold they would freeze over.

Though there had been no running water for a bathroom like she had seen in Vladivostok, there was a small room built at the end of the house. Designed so that any accumulation could be cleaned out below, there was little odor. Freezing in the winter, by spring, all cleanings were transported to be used as fertilizer in the fields.

Underneath one corner of the house was a protected stall where hay and Papa's horse were kept. There were horses kept in the barn that were used to pull the sleigh, but this horse was special. No one but Papa was allowed to ride this horse. He always rode alongside the sleigh or carriage, depending upon the season, escorting his family to church every Sunday that he was home. The family attended the Russian Orthodox Church faithfully every Sunday. Marie particularly like to join in the singing.

Marie watched the shadows as the kerosene lantern, suspended above, swayed with the movement of the boat. The fumes burned her eyes, but she was accustomed to that. They had used kerosene in the Arctic too, or, when they ran out, the natives had taught them to use seal oil lamps. Back home, the long winter nights were dimly lit by the glow of the kerosene lamps as she spun flax into linen and wool into yarn that would be woven on the loom. It seemed so long ago. How she yearned for the evenings she had spent with her family talking and singing.

All Marie had ever known was work. From the time she got up in the morning until she fell into bed every night, she worked. From early childhood, she helped with household tasks until old enough to work outside. Everybody had to work in order to survive.

In the early spring, men, women, and children cleaned out the winter's accumulation of manure and straw in the barns. Buckets were filled and dumped into a two-wheeled cart pulled by one horse. One of the boys usually led the horse pulling the cart into the field. He would jerk the string that tipped the contents of the box into piles spaced around the field.

Marie still seemed to smell the over-powering stench of the enclosed barns as she shoveled layer after layer of rotting straw and manure into the buckets. She much preferred to work out in the open field in the fresh air helping the other women spread the piles of manure. The manure, human and animal, was the only fertilizer they had to enrich the soil. Their winter's supply of food for themselves and their animals depended upon the success of each year's crops. At Koluchin Bay there had been no planting. During the brief summer, only twelve to fifteen inches of tundra ever thawed. With the soil so thin, only lichens and a few tiny plants thrived.

Along with the wheat, rye, flax, barley and other grains, gardens were planted. Marie and her sisters sowed corn, potatoes, peas, onions, beets, cucumbers and other vegetables. There were entire fields of rutabagas and turnips. At that time farm machinery was widely used in European Russia, but there was a lack of machinery and money east of the Ural Mountains. Consequently, manual labor was the method of cultivation and the only option they had. Everyone suffered from stiff and sore muscles in the spring when the land was plowed and planted, but soon everyone became hardened and seasoned to the hard work.

As early in the spring as possible, the women tapped the sap of the birch trees. Only in early spring did the sap provide a much sought after syrup to use on bread and hotcakes.

When crops had grown a few inches, Marie and her sisters, along with the other women, would systematically weed the fields. Wearing wrappers of homespun fabric that tied like a sack, they pulled the weeds. Carrying them in the front of the wrapper-apron, they dumped the weeds alongside the cultivated fields and stretched their aching backs. Marie was glad that her wrapper had long sleeves and a high collar protecting her from the swarming, ravenous mosquitoes looking for an easy meal.

Now, lying on the bunk, her skin began itching with her just thinking about the numerous mosquito bites that had been inflicted on her exposed flesh. A cloud of hungry, buzzing mosquitoes was one thing that Koluchin Bay and Antipina had in common.

Work was unending. After the weeds were under control, Marie went into the woods with the other women and children to strip bark from the birch trees. Loosening the bark with a knife, they removed it by gently separating the bark layer from the tree trunks. Bark from the smaller trees was tied into square bundles to await the buyer from town. He would pay them a few kopeks and deliver the bark to a factory in Tyumen where it was used for tanning hides.

Everyone looked forward to the visit of the bark buyer because he brought along news and gossip from other communities. There were so few diversions from the daily work that Marie would sidle up as close as she could to the bark wagon to listen to the latest news. Marie hoped that one day she would be able to read like her papa so she could understand the newspapers from Tobolsk that Papa occasionally brought home. But girls were expected to stay home and take care of the family. It was unheard of that they should go to school. It was simply not necessary that they be able to read and write. Marie had determined deep within that some day she would learn. She was young, but already too wise to speak of her ambition.

The bark that was not purchased by the buyer was put to soak in water for two weeks or more until the black outer layer came loose and the long white stringers that remained became soft and pliable. Some stringers would be woven into mats that were used as wrappers for supplies and other items that were transported. The longer narrow strips that were ten to twelve feet long were made into bark ropes. Bark ropes were in great demand for tying the bark mats as well as for other uses around the farm. Much of the mat and rope weaving was done in the winter. Women in the community counted on Papa to buy their mats and ropes or trade them for much needed items. How Marie missed him when he was gone on those trading trips.

In late spring the bleating of sheep emanating from the sheep barn usually signaled the beginning of sheep shearing. Shearing was a dirty, dusty job, and the rank smelling sheep put up a fight when it came their turn to be sheared. Alexi and Papa were very gentle with the sheep. They would catch one and set it down between their legs with its front legs up in the air. Starting at the neck, they would cut the wool off with a pair of hand held shears. When they finished the neck, they would clip the front legs and stomach before standing the sheep on its back legs to do the back and hindquarters last.

Marie would gather the warm, newly shorn fleeces and tie them into a bundle. The bales would be stored until later in the fall when they would be carded and spun into yarn to be eventually woven into cloth from which most of their warmer clothing was made. The lanolin from the sheep fleece made Marie's hands soft.

When she was little, Marie had asked,"Papa, doesn't it make the sheep cold when we cut their warm wool coats?" She watched as the forlorn clipped sheep huddled together in a corner of the pen. They looked so naked without their wool.

Papa answered, "They will quickly grow a new coat. That is why we shear them in the spring after it gets warm. If we left their heavy coats all summer, they would be too hot, and if we sheared them in the fall, they would freeze. They will have time to grow a new coat for winter." Papa was so wise about so many things.

"Marie, your mouth is blue," teased Anna.

"Yours is too," laughed Marie.

Anna, Barbara, and Marie had been picking and eating the delicious wild blueberries. In summer, wild strawberries, blackberries, blueberries, and raspberries were plentiful in the woods and along the rivers. The girls gathered them to make jam preserves to eat during the long cold winter. There were sufficient blueberries that they could store them in a fifty-gallon, wooden barrel.

Cranberry bushes covered with cranberries were easily uprooted after frost in the fall. The bushes were hung from the rafters in the barn. The berries were used when needed and the bushes fed to the cattle.

Tillable land was too valuable to plant domestic varieties, so wild berries were gathered every summer. Papa often said, "If we just had more land, we could grow more crops and have more to sell."

Marie did not realize it at the time, but those words were to have a great impact on her later. Papa had always worried about providing well for his family. How she wished they owned more land so Papa would not have to be gone all winter.

"Elizabeth, you are picking the wrong kind of mushrooms," Marie cautioned her younger sister as they gathered mushrooms to preserve in a barrel. "Some of the mushrooms you have in your basket are poisonous."

Sorting the mushrooms in Elizabeth's basket, she showed her the difference between those that were safe and those that were not. A mistake could mean death to someone if he was careless. Elizabeth was six years younger than Marie and had not been collecting mushrooms before. Marie sighed as she thought of how many mushrooms it took to fill a barrel and how far into the forest they would have to walk to pick enough for their winter supply. They had to watch for bears, so they took their dogs with them to, hopefully, scare off any bears they might meet. There were wolves as well, but they never saw them in the daytime. Folk tales of the "wood demon" and "river nymphs" inhabiting the forests made the woods more scary.

Seasons changed, but always there was much to do. Each new season brought a different kind of work to be done.

Summer showers meant good crops. Usually ten to twenty inches of moisture fell in the form of rain or snow in their community. The Zimin's patch of soil was fertile and produced abundantly when watered. Drought brought hardship and bare survival. Papa had dug wells to irrigate some fields, but mostly just the vegetable plots. Cooking and drinking water came from the creek, but they did not drink much water, preferring to drink tea. For guests, the tea was made from carefully rationed tea leaves. For the family, simply slicing some off a tea brick would do.

In late summer when the cabbages were ready to be harvested, they would be cut from the stalks, loaded onto a cart and delivered to the kitchen. Half of the cabbages were made into sauerkraut, and the other half quartered and stored in a barrel. The sauerkraut was made by shredding the cabbage and layering it in a wooden barrel, salting each layer before another layer was added, until the barrel was full. A board with a weight was placed on top to submerge the cabbage in its own juice. The scum that accumulated at the top of the barrel was skimmed as the fermentation process turned the cabbage into sauerkraut. Marie wrinkled her nose at the pungent, sour odor. How could anything that tasted so good smell so bad?

In addition to gathering food for the family during the summer, they had to gather food for the horses, sheep, pigs, cows, and chickens. Work was never-ending.

Swinging a scythe to cut hay for the livestock made Marie's arms very strong and put callouses on her hands. Before winter set in, all of the family, except Mama and baby Peter, went into the fields to cut and stack the hay in midsummer to give the pastures a chance to grow more. When all their hay was cut, Alexi would hire out to other farmers who did not have help at home. For the equivalent of about fifty cents a day, he worked from dawn till dark. Alexi, who was married, could not make enough from his allotment, so he frequently worked for other families who had no sons or whose sons were too young. He also helped on the family farm, especially when Papa was gone.

When the grain ripened, everyone again went into the fields with their scythes. Clasping the hand grip on the long, curved, wooden handle attached to a 30-inch curved razor sharp blade, Marie swung the scythe close to the ground, cutting a swath of grain as wide as the blade of the scythe. For the first day or two, her shoulders and arms felt as though they would fall off, but the stiffness quickly subsided once she started work each morning. She soon developed a smooth rhythm swinging pattern that made harvesting much easier.

When the wheat was cut, others would tie it into bundles. In the evening, they would carry the bundles and place them together, forming big shocks all over the field. In the fall, they hauled the sheaves close to the village and arranged the shocks into a large stack. In early winter, the women took the bundles to a special threshing building and made a fire in the stove to dry the grain to prevent moisture from causing it to mold as well as making it easier to separate the wheat from the chaff.

The dried stalks of grain were then beaten with a stick to knock the grain off the stems. Most of the Russian peasants had to do this by hand, but a few farmers had a machine that performed this operation. After the grain was separated from the stalk, they would toss it into the air so that the wind would separate kernels from chaff. Marie could remember how itchy this process was. Irritating bits of chaff, swirled by gusts of wind, found their way under the tightest of garments. After separation, the kernels were then packed into clean sacks and hauled to the storage building to await grinding.

The storage barn was a long building with many bins for wheat, rye, barley, and corn. All were kept separate. When loading the bins, Marie would sometimes have to cover her face with a cloth to keep out the grain dust.

For as long as she could recall, Marie was aware of the windmills twirling in the wind. They powered the wooden blocks that crushed the grain with a crunching, gnashing noise while producing the flour used in baking. Some of the farmers used horses to turn the milling blocks to grind the grain. A horse was hitched to a long pole that extended from the center of the top circular grinding block. A child would drive the horse around and around in a circle, turning the grinding block and crushing the grain. Some peasants had only a large mortar and pestle to use.

Flax to spin linen cloth was pulled in the fall and dried. As soon as it was dried, the seeds were threshed out. There was a special tool to pull through the stems. When the strands were separated, only the fibers to make fine linen thread remained. When first woven, the linen was a dingy gray. The cloth was taken to the river and pounded, rinsed, pounded some more, then laid out to dry in the sun, which bleached it white. From this, they made towels, blouses, underwear, tablecloths, scarves, bed linens and whatever was needed. There was no problem selling the material left over after home needs were met. Marie spent many hours preparing thread and crocheting.

Sweeping in from the north, the first snow storm triggered the butchering of several pigs. Curing the pork was necessary to preserve it. The pork hams and sides were first salted and then hung in the smokehouse to slowly cure. The intestines of the pig were thoroughly cleaned to stuff for sausages.

Boiling the pig's head to make headcheese was a revolting task. Marie used a stick to keep the head rolled over so the gaping, accusing pig's eyes were submerged. The boiling water made it difficult to keep the head turned upside down. How could something that looked so horrible taste so good?

Sheep and calves were butchered and the meat hung in the meathouse as soon as the weather was sufficiently cold to keep the meat from spoiling. The hides were tanned and made into shoes, boots, and harnesses.

The abundance of fish in the river provided another source of meat for the family and their dogs. One of Marie's favorite times with her father was fishing for sturgeon in the river. Papa had his own secret bait he would use to catch sturgeon. He released the fish into a small pond, and as soon as freeze-up started, he would re-catch the fish and freeze them. Not only did he supply the family, but found a ready market for any surplus sturgeon, which was a delicacy highly sought.

The sub-zero temperatures brought about a change in their work. The men, wearing heavy coats, woolen caps and mittens, as well as wool-lined boots, took care of the stock and performed the multitude of chores outside. Sometimes the snow depth was above boot-top, but they had no snowshoes or skis to ease their tasks.

The women remained indoors, spinning and weaving the wool,

linens, and the five-by-ten foot mats used for wrapping items; there were no cardboard cartons. There was always work to do from the time they arose before daylight until long after dark in the late afternoon.

While spinning wool and making mats, the women would sit close to the fire to stay warm. Singing helped make the time go faster, and how Marie loved to sing. She had a beautiful voice; in fact, a neighbor claimed she sang like a bird. Often the neighbor women would bring their weaving, and they all worked together, making a social occasion out of it and catching up on the latest gossip.

Marie remembered one occasion very well,though she was only about nine at the time.

"Epistina, did you hear that Gregory Novykh has been run out of Pokrovskoe by some local men?" asked a visitor. (He was commonly known as Rasputin, a term that means dissolute.) "That womanizer went too far in his carousing, and the council asked him to leave."

By the scowl on her mother's face, Marie knew that she did not approve of the discussion in front of her daughters.

Barbara spoke up, "When my friend and I visited with him and were guests in his home, he was very hospitable and friendly."

"That may very well be," sniffed another neighbor as she ran her shuttle across the loom. "He claims to be a monk and has the power to heal people, but he spends so much time drinking and chasing women, nobody trusts him."

"His wife served us tea, and he wasn't drunk then,"defended Barbara. "We all had our pictures taken together."

Barbara rose and pulled out a box of personal items. She passed around the picture of the long-haired, self-proclaimed monk with the hypnotic eyes.

The first lady, studying the picture, snorted, "He looks innocent enough here. But thank goodness, he's left the neighborhood. Good riddance!"

In her early teen years, Barbara had decided to become a nun. She walked from monastery to monastery, learning more about the calling. When she and a girl friend returned from their travels of a year, she brought a large icon – three feet by three feet – which she gave to Elancko Celo, their Russian Orthodox Church. One of their last stops had been at Pokrovskoe, Rasputin's home, not far from Antipina. By then Barbara had decided that the lifestyle of a nun was too reclusive for her. "It was like being in quarantine." Instead she worked helping her father deliver his goods.

Mr. Zimin bought the first sewing machine ever seen in that part of the country, and Barbara spent a good deal of time sewing costumes for the villagers to put on a pageant at Christmas for the very first time. This challenged her sewing skills but she worked day and night to get the garments finished. She was paid a small amount. Marie sewed on all the costume buttons, but nobody offered to pay her.

Marie could not remember a time when she had not worked. Each year brought added chores and responsibilities. With the weaving, the younger children threaded the shuttles through the upright threads on the loom, while the older girls set the tension and worked the design into the cloth. Anna, being older, started weaving before Marie. Marie was so glad when she became old enough to create the design and Elizabeth had to thread the shuttles.

So much had to be done to provide the warm clothing so vital to existence. In Antipina, Marie had worn a woolen coat lined with sheepskin to break the cold Arctic wind that blew hundreds of miles across the tundra and high plains of Western Siberia. Because of the north/south position of the Ural Mountains, there were no natural barriers to protect the flatland plains from the fierce, bone-chilling blizzards. In early fall, the rivers would start to freeze and shortly thereafter would be completely frozen over.

Brief hours of daylight during the winter brought little comfort from the frequent blizzards and bitter cold. At least during the winter in Antipina there had been a few hours of daylight. At Koluchin Bay for almost two months there was no more than a dull strip of gray at noon. How lonesome it had been, living in the dark, with only native women, who did not understand her culture or language, with whom to visit.

Chester stirred beside her and snuggled closer. She put her arms around him to settle him. As she looked at her sleeping child, she was again saddened by the thought that he would not experience the close family gatherings that she had enjoyed as a child growing up. All he had ever known was the limited companionship of Eskimo children, Carl, and herself.

What fun she had when her mother's two sisters and their families would come to visit and stay in their home. Aunt Olga lived in Tyumen so had to travel over sixty miles to join the family. Aunt Alexandra lived nearby in Antipina, so she came more often. There was much laughter and singing, and on holidays they did not have to work so hard.

On special occasions, just outside the village, the men would gather to race their horses or watch others race. They bet on the outcomes and cheered their respective choices. The younger women listened raptly as a volunteer fortune teller read their palms and described the men they would marry. The older women gossiped and prepared vast amounts of food. They all drank kvass which was a soft drink made from black bread, yeast, sugar and currants. The men usually preferred the home-brewed beer.

And there were games that everyone joined in. Marie remembered the happy, warm feelings she had at those special family and neighborhood gatherings. There were not many occasions to get together – everyone was too busy.

With pleasure, Marie thought of her only toy – a rag doll her mother had made. Gentle Mama, Epistina, was always so busy, but never too busy for a kind word of encouragement. If just once more she could sit and watch Mama brush her long, brown hair with the reddish highlights, so much like Marie's own. Mama was shorter than Marie and somewhat rounded by years of babies and good cooking. Her face showed the struggle, but to Marie it would always be beautiful. If only she could talk with Mama and show her Chester.

It had been three long years since she had talked with or shared her feelings with anyone. Carl did not understand how hard it had been for her. It did seem like she had been faced with more than her share of unusual circumstances. Each decision she had made only lead to more problems. Had she been wrong about wanting more from life than just following in her mother's footsteps? Ever since she was eleven and became the first girl in her village to attend school because she wanted so desperately to read and write like Papa, she was determined to be successful. Withstanding the taunts and ridicule from a classroom full of boys had toughened her resolve to show everyone that she could endure hardship to get what she wanted. She wasn't at all sure now where her hard-headed determination was going to lead her.

The house that Marie's father built for his family.

CHAPTER FOUR

SCHOOL DAYS REMEMBERED

"You're lazy!"

"You just want to go to school so you don't have to work!"

It had been years ago, but the stinging words still rang in her ears. Marie was only eleven years old and fiercely determined to learn to read and write.

One day in 1910, Barbara, who played such a major part in some of the biggest events in Marie's life, called Marie and said, " I have been talking to the teacher at the seminary. She wants you or Anna to start school in the fall."

Barbara had learned to read from an old man in the village, but she had never learned to write. She felt the limits in her life because of her lack of education and she was determined some one in her family should have the opportunity to be educated.

Marie was delighted! She had always wanted to be able to read and write like Papa, but it was a very revolutionary idea. There were no educational facilities for girls in Antipina. Indeed, why would this tiny village with its traditional life-style need to educate future housewives? There were only about one hundred thousand schools in all Russia, six thousand of them in Siberia, almost entirely for boys, and provided through the church. A few seminaries for girls in Western Russia catered to the elite.

"Marie, why do you want to go to school?" asked Maria Dimetrya, the nun who taught elementary level.

"I want to read and write like my papa. I want to be able to read the newspaper to learn what is going on without having to hear it from peddlers," she nervously replied. Grim determination was etched in every line of her body as she attempted to explain why it was so important for her to go to school.

The teacher was interviewing Anna, too. Marie worried. Anna was older and most indifferent but had come at Barbara's suggestion that she, too, might receive an education. The nun made it very clear that only one girl could be accepted.

Marie nervously twisted her apron as Anna responded to the teacher's questions. A silence fell on the classroom until the teacher, in deep thought, began to drum her fingers on her desk. Marie realized she was holding her breath waiting for the nun to make the decision.

Finally, she spoke, "Marie, do you realize that there are thirty boys in class, and that you will be the first girl to ever attend school in Antipina? You will have to work hard on your lessons."

Marie was ecstatic. She could barely contain her excitement as she squealed, "Thank you! I will work hard!" She would make Papa proud of her.

Marie spent every minute possible studying her lessons day and night. Even in her dreams she was taunted by the cruel derision of the boys. The teasing hurt. She was not lazy. She would learn! She knew the boys were just repeating what some of the villagers were saying, but she was not lazy! In the summer she would work as hard as ever. She would show them!

But she had not realized how hard it would be for her to go to school. Ambition burned fiercely within. Only at unguarded moments did the hurt seep in. Her tears were shed in private. Each tear strengthened her resolve to excel.

Thirty boys to one girl was impossible odds. Realizing that Marie was being teased unmercifully, the teacher invited Marie to move into the living quarters that adjoined the classroom. Marie's entire world became the small rooms in which she felt so gigantic, for she loomed almost a foot above the teacher and the nun's mother, who did all the cooking and cleaning, leaving Marie free to study full time.

Since Marie's home was seven miles away, it was much more convenient for her. That one of the Zimina girls should receive an education was a source of great pride, and the family gladly supplied food for the teacher. They supported the idea that Marie should be able to read and write.

Marie's life changed so much after she started school. She studied in the living quarters and had her lessons in the evening. At times she would hear the boys at recess, but there was no recess for her – she had too much to learn.

Many nights the sound of her book crashing to the floor awakened her as she had fallen asleep studying. Groggily, she would get up and stumble off to bed. It was often very late, and her pillow was much softer than a book on which to sleep.

By early spring of 1912, she had whizzed through the first two levels of the three required in elementary school. She wanted to complete the third level before summer vacation so that she could qualify for the final examination given by the government. She just knew she could do it!

Maria Dimetrya, her teacher, laughed and said, "Enough is enough! Two years in one and now you want to do the third. You can master it next fall. Why are you in such a big hurry? The books will still be here when you return."

When spring semester ended, Marie returned home and spent the rest of the summer helping plant, harvest, and prepare for the winter months. She sang all the time because she knew how to read and write and now she was learning so much about the Bible and Christ.

Marie was aware that her efforts had surpassed any that the boys expended, though the boys were motivated less from eagerness to learn than they were by the compulsory conscription into the military. Many times she had heard her papa say, "Boys must be able to read and to remember what officers say."

After twenty-one years of age, each able male must spend six years of active service with nine years of reserves in the Russian army. However, this was cut to four years with a primary education, two years with secondary, and only six months if a university graduate. There were exceptions depending upon family need and the fulfilling of village quotas. Brother Alexi had completed the elementary level and had served his time in the military.

By early spring of 1913, her unceasing efforts had prepared Marie to complete the elementary level and to go to take the governmental competency exams to get her diploma.

"Hurry, Papa!" Marie excitedly told her father as she pulled on her wool coat and gloves.

They were leaving for Baykalova, thirty miles away, for her to take her test and she wanted to get started. Spring thaw had come early and the yard was a sea of mud. Thank goodness, the picket fence, made of closely spaced wooden slats driven into the ground, had kept the livestock from around the house. Outside the gate, the yard was mire with boot-top level muck churned up by cows and horses.

Jumping into the cart with her little satchel of clothes that she would need for her brief stay, Marie sat down beside her father. She was so elated, but a little nervous about the upcoming tests! She just had to do well on the tests! She had studied so hard! She had to show everyone that she was not lazy!

Squishing noises from the horse's hooves slogging through the mud accompanied the creaking of the wheels as the cart advanced slowly out of the yard. Marie waved goodbye to her mother and sisters. Alexi, who had come over to help because Papa would be gone, was already in the barns feeding the animals. Her father sat proudly beside her. It was his daughter who had been the first girl to attend school in the village, and now she was going to take her tests.

While the horse and cart slowly made their way toward the ferry, Marie and her father talked about his winter's trading. Because she had learned math, she understood what her father was explaining about buying and selling goods. Every moment with Papa was special to her.

"Looks like the river's pretty high," her papa commented as they neared the river raft crossing.

In spring the rivers often flooded out of their banks as the winter snow melted. Marie's heart sank as she looked at all that water. How could they cross that angry, boiling river? After all her studying was the Tobol River going to keep her from taking her tests and getting her diploma?

When they stopped the mud-spattered cart at the edge of the river bank, the ferryman poked his head out of his cabin. "Will you be crossin' today or waitin' till morning?"

"We need to cross this afternoon, if possible. We need to be in Baykalova early tomorrow," Ivan Zamin answered.

"Pretty risky, been a lot of trees and limbs floatin' down the river. Almost got tipped over yesterday."

Marie looked out over the water where she could see a big tree floating by with its limbs flailing the water like huge arms. If they couldn't cross the river, she would have to wait until next year to take her tests.

"Will it be any better tomorrow?"

"Can't rightly say. It could be better or it could be worse," the ferryman shrugged as he spit a big chew of bark resin on the ground, dribbling some in his long gray beard.

"Then we will go today," Papa stated as he climbed down off the cart. "Marie, step down so we can load the horse and cart."

Marie surveyed the frightening scene before her. The roaring, churning river tugged at the flimsy log raft held together by leather thongs and bark rope. A rope was threaded between two pulleys attached to the raft, and each end was tied to trees on both sides of the river. The thought of riding that raft to the other side of the river scared Marie. But her father thought it would be safe enough. Trusting Papa, she didn't say a word.

Rolling his eyes, the horse shied nervously and snorted. Papa reassured the animal as he led it onto the shifting swaying craft. When the horse put his front foot on the deck of the unsteady raft, the edge settled under his weight. Rearing, he almost knocked Papa into the water.

Never letting go of the horse's bridle, Papa calmed the trembling horse and finally coaxed the skittish animal pulling the cart onto the bobbing raft. Marie's stomach knotted in fear as she gingerly stepped onto the unsteady planks and the ferryman followed. How were they ever going to make it across without drowning?

Ivan Zimin tied the horse securely and then turned his attention to his terrified daughter, reassuring her. Marie grasped his arm with an iron grip, too petrified to let go.

Releasing the raft from the dock, the ferryman held on tightly to the tow rope. Instantly, the river seized the craft. The rope snapped tight. The jolt startled Marie and caused her to lose her balance. She clung more tightly to her father's arm to keep from falling. She knew her end was near. The horse tried to rear but was tied too closely to the rail. Steadying Marie with one hand, Papa calmed the snorting, frantic horse with the other hand.

The thundering, snarling river buffeted them and tossed them around like a piece of cork. Pulling the rope hand over hand, the ferryman swiped his wet face with his shoulder. Water sprayed up over the front end drenching their clothes. Marie closed her eyes and held onto her father for dear life. We're going to drown, she thought, as the tight knot in her stomach threatened to make her throw-up.

"Oh, God! Save us from this raging beast!" she prayed.

The ferryman hollered! Marie opened her eyes! Right in front of them was a huge tree with branches thrashing and clawing at the muddy, rolling water as it was swiftly being carried downstream. The ferryman stopped pulling, and the raft started backing up as the current tugged it back towards the shore.

The huge tree swept by them, narrowly missing their flimsy craft. Papa unclenched Marie's hand from his arm and, hand over hand, helped pull the ferry across the raging river. When they finally bumped the shore on the other side, Marie jumped off onto firm ground. Her knees gave out from under her. She was shaking so badly she could barely stand. She wanted her diploma, but she wasn't sure she would go through that again for it!

After unloading the sweating, spray-covered horse and cart from the ferry, Ivan Zimin paid the ferryman and they continued on their way – wet, exhausted and glad to put the harrowing experience behind them. They would wait for the river to subside before they tried it again.

Marie passed her tests. In fact, she had been so well prepared that they had seemed easy to her. Some of the government tests had included memorization of long passages from the Bible as well as math, science, reading, spelling, and grammar...none of which had been a problem.

The papers were corrected immediately, and they told her that she had passed with the top score in every subject, and that she had won an award that they would mail to her.

The award never did come. But she was happy. She had proved that Marie Zimina was not lazy!

She enjoyed being with her family that summer, but there was no time for socializing. By the time August arrived, it was time for her to go to Tyumen where she would attend a second level school.

CHAPTER FIVE

MORE LEARNING: INCLUDING ABOUT RASPUTIN

"Yes," Marie smiled to herself wryly, "I thought an education would give me all the answers. It only made me want to learn more."

Making the decision to go to school in Tyumen the fall of 1913 was not too difficult. Her former teacher lived there as well as her aunt with whom she stayed. Tyumen was an experience in itself, being the oldest city in Siberia and the western terminus of the river vessels carrying cargo from Omsk and Tomsk.

With the aid of the teacher she selected the best second level gymnasium, as the schools were called.

"Aunt Olga, a friend of mine at school has asked me to move into her home with her family. They live close to the school and we can study together," pleaded Marie.

"But you have only been with us for two months, Marie."

"I know. But it would be easier for me to go to school if I didn't have to walk so far. I would have more time to study," explained Marie.

"I guess you could try it, and if it doesn't work out, you are always welcome back here," sighed Aunt Olga, "but you are only fourteen and you must be very careful."

Marie was strongly determined to spend all her time studying, preparing for the second level exams. There was no religion in this school – only math, science, world geography, history, grammar and Latin. Oh, but Latin was hard! It was so different!

And she continued diligently studying while remaining in her friend Maria's home for two years, though she felt the younger brother was weird. He talked to his pigeons all day long.

She still traveled home during vacations and summers to help out. Completing the four years in three, she passed her competency examinations with no problem.

Marie had no desire to stop her education at that point. She would go to Turinsk to complete her studies. By now she was accustomed to living away from home and rarely got homesick. She never had time while in school and spending summers at home kept her in touch.

The next fall she boarded the steamboat bound for Turinsk. Tightly gripping her satchel, she looked around at the Russian peasants of varied nationalities, Gypsies, and soldiers who came aboard with her. Now at sixteen, she could not help feeling a bit lost. She had been warned not to speak to strangers and there was not a soul she knew.

The whistle blew. Black smoke belched from the big smokestack as the coal fired engines beat a rhythmic cadence underfoot. The big paddle wheel slowly started to turn, pushing the steamboat away from the dock. Every turn of the paddle wheel propelled them further out into the river. Marie felt much more secure on this boat than she had the raft a couple of years ago.

Vibrations from the throbbing engines could be felt as she leaned against the railing. The golden and red trees reminded Marie that fall had arrived and before long the cold Siberian wind would be blowing in from the north. When the river froze, the river boat would be tied up until the river thawed in the spring.

Marie meditated on how her life had been controlled by the seasons. Spring and summer meant hard work in the fields; winter had been a time for weaving, crocheting, sewing, spinning. August meant starting school and that was her favorite time of year.

Throughout the hundred mile boat trip, Marie watched the changing countryside. She had always wanted to travel and see new places. But doubts assailed her. Will the school in Turinsk accept my application? What will happen if I can't find a room? What if someone steals my money? Unconsciously, she clutched her purse more tightly. There were so many unanswered questions racing through her mind.

Maybe Mama was right. Maybe I shouldn't have traveled so far from home for school. One hundred sixty long miles separated her from her family.

Her fears were set to rest upon arrival at Turinsk. She located a room in a boardinghouse operated by an elderly lady, Cederosa. There were several other school girls living there and they said it was a good place to stay.

Her nervousness at the interview subsided when the president of the college assured her that with her high grades she would be accepted into the third level gymnasium.

The music teacher, a nun, tested Marie's voice and placed her in the choir, which sang every Sunday in the Russian Orthodox Church. Marie felt right at home. She loved singing. On Sundays all the girls dressed in brown dresses with white aprons for church. On school days they wore brown dresses with black aprons. The school was very strict about their appearance and dress. One time, one of the other girls wore a plain dress to school and was sent home to change into her brown uniform. Everyone looked so nice dressed alike.

Marie's favorite class was music which she had twice a week. When she was chosen to sing a duet with a classmate for confession, she was ecstatic. They would practice all week for their Sunday duet. Sometimes they were asked to sing at funerals. The time at school just sped by.

But once in awhile loneliness would creep in because she missed her family. On the spur of the moment she decided to go home for Christmas holidays. There was a train leaving for Tyumen-Ekatenburg, no matter that it was a freight with only two wagons for passengers. She bought her ticket and was at last on her way home to see her folks.

The swaying of the cars, the snow gently falling outside the window, and the clickity-clack of the iron wheels as they rolled down the track, lulled Marie to sleep. All of a sudden, there was a grinding and screeching of metal as Marie was thrown from her seat.

Panic reigned. People were screaming and crying as they were bounced like rubber balls inside the car. Careening wildly, the car flew off the track and came to rest on its side. Moans and groans came from the bruised, the more severely injured and dying passengers.

Frightened, but alive, Marie, clawing her way out from under some luggage, crawled shakily out of the car. Outside she could see that the cars had telescoped into each other when the train hit an avalanche caused by heavy snows. One of the passenger wagons rested almost on top of the other. Marie immediately got to work, helping sort through the tangled metal and shattered wood searching for survivors. People who were not hurt assisted the injured.

By now it was snowing heavily and everyone was cold, soaked, and tired. Marie shivered. Creeping back into the car to look for her satchel, she realized how lucky she had been to have only bumps and bruises. Luggage was strewn all over. Bags had popped open and the contents scattered about. Finding her bag, still intact, she groped her way out. A conductor informed the passengers another train was coming to take them back to Ekatenburg.

It was several hours before the replacement train arrived. Since the tracks had been swept away, there obviously would be no through trains. While Marie sat in abject misery, she wondered, "Who is responsible? Would a snow fence have prevented this useless waste of life and time?" Of course, there was no answer to her questions but she did know that hasty building methods meant railroad beds were not firmly compacted, and washouts and avalanches occurred frequently. Light weight rails and ties that were too widely spaced added more problems and delays for the train. At long last she heard the distant whistle of the relief train.

When Marie finally made it to Tyumen, she caught a ride with a farmer headed for Antipina. She was chilled, wet, and exhausted. After she reached home, she became very ill. Her neck swelled; she lost her voice. Her vacation was miserable.

While she was at home, her father announced, "Rasputin is dead!"

Though Marie had never met him, she had the picture of him taken with Barbara and his two daughters. She vaguely remembered the criticism of her mother's friends. He had been forced to leave his home at Pokrovskoe because of his drinking and womanizing. It was said there was no woman, whatever the age, safe from his hypnotic eyes and lustful charisma. He wandered from place to place. His various adventures landed him at court where his crude manner and extreme arrogance repelled, but attracted, the females and made him detested by the males. Empress Alexandra was enthralled by him. With his long hair he looked like a monk. He ate no pastries, sweets or meat. He no longer drank vodka but did drink great amounts of Port and Madeira. A master of hypnotism, he convinced the Empress he could heal her hemophiliac son. It was true; the child did rest easier after one of Rasputin's sessions.

The Empress Alexandra, wife of the Czar, was the daughter of Louis IV, Grand Duke of Hesse, a small German state, and the granddaughter of Queen Victoria of England. She hated the governmental body, the Duma. She felt they had usurped much of her husband's power. She also dominated her husband, the Czar. She was easy prey for a master of deceit like Rasputin. The Czar, Nicholas II, left the affairs of state up to his wife while he conducted the military in the war with Germany. Seizing the opportunity, Rasputin manipulated Alexandra into removing all the ministers who opposed him from state affairs and replaced them with his choices.

The government soon fell apart. By the fall of 1916, it was intolerable. Rasputin was charged with being in league with the Germans and in December, a coalition of aristocrats poisoned him. He did not die so they beat and shot him. Still not dead, they bound his feet with a weight and threw him into the river to drown. The body was eventually placed in a shallow grave where it was exhumed some time later and finally burned.

Since Rasputin had lived so close by, the news traveled fast through the community. Neighbors felt sorry for his wife and children, but no regret at his passing.

By the time Marie was well enough to travel, the trains were running again. Once back in Turinsk, classes went on as usual. She continued studying hard, but found time to participate in a club whose purpose was to make floral decorations for the church. She continued singing, read many books, and crocheted table cloths. Though she did not care to act in the plays, she did help produce them. Sometimes she sold candy at school events. But she never learned to dance, though often later she wished she had. And she made flowers for the church for Easter.

Everyone looked forward to Easter. Marie loved the excitement and gaiety. Friends and family traveled to visit each other. The horses' harnesses were decorated with bells that jingled as they ran. Sleigh rides were given to everyone and each driver tried to outdo the others in gaudy decorations on the horses and sleighs as well. What a joy to snuggle down under the fur robe in the sleigh as the horses sped across the snow covered plain. Wind stung her cheeks as she peered out from beneath the fur rug. The horses' breath formed a steamy cloud as they raced. The exhilarating sleigh rides always put everyone in a happy mood. Women had new colorful dresses and almost everyone went to church. This was the biggest holiday of the year. The priests charged a little money for the special services on Easter. Sometimes they had all night services. Icons were carried from one family to another and the people would pray to the icons and hope for a miracle.

Before Easter the women were busy cooking. Special cakes (kyliches) were baked. For holidays they used white flour for their cookies and cakes; the rest of the year they used only their home ground grain. Also they served tea made from tea leaves. Before Easter, people would not eat meat, butter, or milk for several weeks.

Marie thought that the people enjoyed their holidays so intensely because they must work so hard the rest of the time just to exist.

Marie sighed and rolled over in her bunk on the BEAR. Time had eluded her at Koluchin Bay. Easter was just a memory, and besides, Easter meant the beginning of spring and at Koluchin Bay there had been only winter and July.

CHAPTER SIX

WATCHING THE CZAR: SINGING FOR LENIN AND TROTSKY

On April 30, 1917, Trotsky and Lenin came to Turinsk. Before they came, the music teacher started the glee club learning revolutionary songs. In a short time, by hard work, they learned several songs and the chorus was drafted to accompany Trotsky and Lenin as they spoke.

Marie remembered telling her mother about it. "We walked from morning to dark from one place to another, singing songs. In the middle of the afternoon, I tripped. I broke the heel off my shoe. Everyone looked at me strangely when I hobbled to keep my place in line. I just kept singing. When I got back, how my legs ached!"

"In between, Trotsy and Lenin gave speeches. They say everybody should be equal; both men and women should own land. It sounds good, but do you think it will happen? Well, anyway, the singing was fun."

From school Marie had learned about Czar Nicholas II. She respected him as the nation's leader, but seldom even thought about him. His political problems with the Duma, or Congress of Soviets – a provisional government set up in response to a rebellion in 1906 that forced the Czar to provide a national constitution – were of no concern to her. Her political interests extended no further than the program the Czar was initiating to provide a universal educational system.

Marie was unaware that the Czar was trying to firmly establish a military dictatorship. He was supported by the upper class or Mensheviks upon whom he bestowed his favors. This group became known as the Whites. Opposing them were many who had long been agitating for rule by the common man, the workers, and the soldiers. Two leaders, whose ideas ran along similar lines but different approaches to accomplishing control by the masses, were to emerge. They were Vladimir Ilich Ulyanov, who assumed the name of Lenin from the Lena River in Siberia where he had been exiled for his part in leading revolts, and Lev Davidovich

Bronstein, son of a Jewish farmer, who was to become known as Trotsky. For his revolutionary efforts, he, too, had been forced to flee.

Meantime, Nicholas was concentrating all his efforts on the war with Germany in 1917. It was not a popular war with the Russian people. Masses were starving and cold; there were some who felt they should be fighting with the Germans against the English. A Council of Workers and Soldiers were opposed to the dictates of the Duma and tired of trying to fight a war with insufficient supplies, a deficient transportation system, and a great sacrifice of manpower. Seizing control of the central power, the Congress, in March, 1917, forced the Czar to abdicate in favor of his brother who refused the position. Thus ended the three hundred year regime of Romanov leadership and the Czarist dictatorship.

For seven months governmental control was in the hands of a weak appointed leader, Kerensky, who was easily uprooted by the daily increasing power of the Bolsheviks under the strong leadership of Lenin and Trotsky. By this time any philosophical differences between them had been resolved as to whether the masses would come to a socialistic lifestyle naturally, or whether force would be necessary to bring this about. The two men actually believed they knew what was best, not only for Russia, but all mankind.

In May, 1917, Marie graduated, having completed the four-year course in two years. She started home from Tyumen. Spring run-off made the rivers high, flooding the roads. Farmers did not go to town in the spring; they were busy at home cleaning barns, getting ready for spring planting. Marie could not get a ride. She had no money to pay someone to drive her. There was no way she could let her parents know – no telephones in Antipina. No mail was getting through. If she intended to go home, she would have to walk the last twenty miles.

Walking was indeed difficult. Where the road was covered with water, she had no idea how deep it might be. Women wore only dresses, so she had to roll her skirt up high and start wading across the water. The mud on the road not covered with water was too deep and slimy to walk on; she had to stay alongside the bank of the river close to the road through the forest. She was worried and scared. The thought of meeting a bear or wolf frightened her. To her great relief she never saw one. But she never saw another human being before she arrived home. Never before had she been so glad to be there!

Marie sent her diploma, along with an application, to an organization in Tobolsk that provided nurses' training. She waited several months.

Meantime, Lenin disbanded the Duma in November, 1917, brutally enforced all opposition and ended war with Germany. Many German prisoners who had been assigned to work on Siberian farms opted to stay. They had been treated so well – plenty of food, whiskey and women. A few of the Russian women left their husbands to be with the ex-prisoners of war. At first the Russian attitude towards the Germans was one of acceptance, but when word trickled home about the treatment of some of the Russian soldiers who had been starved, forced to pick up garbage to eat, worked until they dropped, and constantly degraded, attitudes changed abruptly.

Civil war broke out between all factions in Western Russia. The strict disciplining of the troops by Trotsky firmly established Lenin as leader of the Bolsheviks, later to be called Communists or Reds, named for the color of the flag of the World Communist Movement. Trotsky was second in command. (He was being groomed to follow Lenin whose health had been deteriorating since an attempted assassin's bullet in 1918. By 1922 he had had several strokes.)

Though the party operated as a dictatorship, within the party itself, criticism was permitted. One to criticize, much to Lenin's annoyance, was a man named Joseph Stalin. As Stalin gained more influence within the party, he challenged Trotsky for party leadership in 1923 and defeated him. Lenin died in 1924; Trotsky tried to regain power, was defeated, and was exiled in 1927. After residing in several countries who invited him to move on, he ended in Mexico where he was assassinated in 1940. Josef Stalin was in full control.

Unaware of the political turmoil, Marie waited impatiently for a reply to her application. No response forthcoming, in early December, 1917, Marie decided to ride along with her father in the sleigh to Tobolsk where he was going to purchase some trade goods.

The crusted snow crunched under the horses' hooves and the sled runners glided easily as they traveled. The cold December air made her cheeks tingle and her nose turn red, but she was happy to spend some time with Papa.

Upon arriving in Tobolsk, Marie went immediately to the nurses' training school. She asked, "What happened? Why haven't I heard from you? I sent in an application months ago; I would like to become a nurse."

A clerk in the office replied, "Your letter and diploma came too late. Classes had already started."

"You could have let me know and returned my diploma," Marie

told the indifferent woman. Marie had badly wanted to join the program to become a nurse and her disappointment was apparent. "I would like my diploma so I can take it home with me."

She had worked too hard for that diploma to entrust it any longer in the school's care. Angrily she took the papers and rejoined Papa who was still busy trading. Deciding a walk might cool her anger she ignored the cold – it was below zero but she was still steaming.

Marie had gone only a short distance when she noticed a large house that was being closely guarded. Looking up at the veranda around the second story, she could see several people talking as they strolled, obviously for exercise.

Staring upward, she heard someone behind her say, "That's Czar Nicholas II and his wife and family. They are being detained, supposedly to protect them from the Germans. If you ask me, they look more like they are prisoners."

The stranger looked up once more, shook her head and went on her way.

Marie watched in fascination. Of course, she had heard about the Czar but never ever imagined she would see him.

That night Marie and her father stayed in a rooming house that was crowded with refugees fleeing from the Communists. There were several families in each room, and many were sleeping on the floor. Marie decided this was not for her. Any thoughts about staying in Tobolsk to find a job were erased by the crowded living conditions. The internal political unrest of the country had finally touched close to home.

Starting back early the next morning Marie could talk with her father alone. She told him what she had seen of the royal family and asked, "What will become of them?"

His response seemed more like a prayer than a statement, "I hope they can find peace and quiet to live out their lives."

Actually the Czar was rather a shy man, not overly intelligent, but a loving family man. His family exiled with him at Tobolsk continued with their lessons and religious training, but without the luxuries to which they were accustomed, though the conditions were not too severe.

Meantime, there were several splinter groups that were trying to help free the Czar. They were hampered by his insistence that he would not leave without his family. Seven people plus entourage would hardly go unnoticed.

The greatest obstacle to any escape was the lack of any coordination or leadership. A man supposedly filling that requirement was

Boris Soloviev, husband of Maria, the oldest daughter of Rasputin. He was an adventurer, son of a farmer, and, at times, a soldier in the Russian army, though he never reached the front. Trained in hypnotism, he met Maria at a spiritualist meeting and they were married on October 15, 1917. They lived for a few weeks at Rasputin's home at Pokrovskloe, near Tobolsk. There he established contact with the Empress through her maid. Mistakenly placing her trust in him, as she had Rasputin, she called their mission to save the Czar, "The Brotherhood of St. John of Tobolsk."

Puzzled that Soloviev chose to move to Tyumen rather than Tobolsk, the royal family did not understand that his intent was to be located at the railhead where all contact and communication must go through him first to reach the Czar. People who had donated money and supplies became suspicious when nothing was happening; they discovered that there never had been any attempt to organize an army to free the Czar. Their communications, most of the money and supplies had never reached the Czar. Meantime, The Solovievs, plus loot, escaped through Siberia to Vladivostok. In the 1930's they toured Europe and the United States with Maria performing as a lion tamer in an act billed as "Daughter of the famous monk whose feats in Russia astonished the world." Retirement found her in Los Angeles, California.

In April, 1918, orders came to bring the Czar to Moscow to stand trial. Alexi, 12, was too ill to be moved. After much discussion and prayer, it was decided that three of the girls, Olga, 22; Tatiana, 20; and Anastasia, 16, would remain with Alexi along with the doctor and maid. Marie, 18, would accompany her parents. Apprehended on the train by a faction of the Red Army, they were imprisoned at Ekaterinburg (now Sverdlosk) and subjected to much humiliation. The girls and Alexi were able to rejoin their parents in May.

The attitude of the guards was beginning to soften toward these people who were suffering adversity with dignity and pride. The commander in charge, a professional soldier, was warned that the Whites, along with support of Czech soldiers, were coming to free the Czar. At midnight in a small room in the basement, the Czar sat, holding his son in his arms. A group of soldiers came in and started shooting. A maid who tried to run was bayoneted; Alexi, not mortally wounded, was grasping his father's lapel as he was shot again. Anastasia, who had only fainted, was clubbed and stabbed.

All the bodies were cut into pieces and placed in a fire to burn. It took three days to destroy the remains and even then it was necessary to douse the larger bones with sulfur. The ashes and remains were dumped down into a mine shaft previously sought for that purpose. The body of the pet dog, Jimmy, was found in the mine, along with the remains of his royal masters.

When the White Army arrived eight days later they found alive only Joy, another pet dog, forlornly searching for her family.

The Reds brutally suppressed all opposition. Ending the war with Germany they turned their attention to bringing the class war into the villages in Western Russia. The wealthy and educated were threatened. Much of the nobility had arisen from military ranks to positions free from tax and military conscription. There was no middle class.

The peasants were not considered by anyone. The war had been unpopular with them. They, and Marie as well, did not understand the Duma. The concern of the peasants and the Zimin family was owning the land they worked. The church, which could have become a dominant factor, provided no leadership. Its influence had waned with the government takeover of education. Severely threatened, it remained aloof from all political involvement. The summer of 1918 civil war broke out between the Red Army, monarchists, nationalists and anarchists and the chaos of revolution was no longer to be a remote rumor.

But in December, 1917, Marie had no inkling of what was to come. She and Papa were trying to get home.

CHAPTER SEVEN

CAUGHT IN A BLIZZARD IN TATAR COUNTRY

The weather was bitterly cold when Marie and Papa left Tobolsk the next morning – about a minus fifty degrees, but the day was calm. However, within a couple hours a slight breeze was becoming a strong wind.

"We need to find shelter. Our horses are too tired," Papa spoke slowly over the now howling wind. Concern etched his brow as he continued, "The only shelter around here is a Tatar village."

Marie shuddered as the cold icy wind blew back a corner of the fur lap robe. She thought about spending the night in a Tatar village. The Tatars spoke a different language and they would not be able to communicate verbally. She felt uneasy about that but the thought of staying with the Tatars made her a lot less nervous than being trapped out on the plain in a blizzard.

Amid icy blasts the Tatars greeted them with words Marie did not know, but the gestures of welcome were easily understood. They showed Papa where he could stable the horses and ushered the miserable, frozen guests into a large two-story house with planked siding. Benches lined all the walls and from the fireplace radiated the most comforting warmth.

Their hostess, dressed in a loose shirt with a vee front and high collar over a calico blouse, trousers tied under the knees, and a kerchief on her head, motioned them to sit on the bench nearest the stove.

Adjoining the fireplace was a brick oven area with a huge iron bowl cemented in for cooking. Marie's mouth watered at the delicious smell arising with the steam. The woman placed gobs of dough into the boiling contents and fluffy dumplings rose to the top.

Looking around the room Marie noted the beautiful hand-made quilts folded upon the chests that sat on some of the benches. These chests contained the personal items of the various family members. Mats or rugs were placed between the chests and the shelves which opened out to become beds.

There were other people in the room. Two little girls with flat braided hair and pigtails were dressed much like their mother. The men wore coats hanging almost to their knees and decorated with buttons on a short waist. Their short, wide breeches were tucked into the tops of boots made of felt and dipped in a tar solution to waterproof them. Those who planned to remain inside had removed their boots and wore heavy woolen socks. Marie had heard they always wore the berets or skull caps they had on their heads; but for severe cold, they exchanged them for heavy fleece lined caps.

Amid all the bustle, Marie discerned that there was to be a wedding. The Tatars were Moslems and the ritual would take place in the mosque, followed by feasting on foods prepared for days in advance, and would include the savory dish now bubbling away.

Marie watched the ceremony with a great deal of interest. The bride wore a velvet headband decorated with beads and metal ornaments. Her dress was colorful with lace and beads, as were those of all the ladies present. All the women wore kerchiefs on their heads, but that of the bride had much more elaborate beadwork. Their boots were of the finest Moroccan leather. Much gaudy jewelry hung around their necks and they used both rouge and lipstick on their faces.

A veil hid the bride's face from the groom and his family. Indeed, the groom had never seen the bride, nor she him. He had paid her father the bride-price for this girl of thirteen, the age most Tatar girls were considered old enough to marry.

The ceremony was quite different from brother Alexi's wedding. As the oldest son Alexi's nuptials had been arranged and he had not been permitted to marry the girl of his choice. Economics was the first consideration and much too important to leave to the young who were much too inexperienced. But Marie thought that Alexi seemed happy with his wife and children.

There was another similarity. Wedding dates must be set so as not to interfere with the important work of the village.

Much feasting and laughter followed the wedding, but there was no music or dancing which Marie assumed would accompany every wedding. These were forbidden by Islam, the Moslem religion; however, some ancient traditional beliefs in spirits still remained and the women played and sang in the privacy of their homes – but never when outsiders were present.

The food was delicious. Mutton was the dominant meat – though they also ate venison and horsemeat. Oh, my! she hoped it wasn't horsemeat! There was also a variety of vegetables.

Vegetables were grown in their gardens when an early spring permitted planting. When late spring cut the growing season too short, they had to resort to cedar nuts for the long winter. Crops had been abundant this year. The fields of rye, barley, oats, and even wheat, had done well. Hard work with wooden plows and wooden harrows with iron teeth had paid off.

Along with some produce there had been much handiwork and dairy products to trade at the annual market which had been at Tyumen this year. Each year the market place varied in location. Primarily agrarian, these people were quick to adopt any new innovations and assimilated the new into the old with ease.

Papa awakened Marie early the next morning. She had slept soundly on the shelf bed her hostess had insisted she use, but Papa had slept rolled in a blanket on the floor. Quickly eating the porridge and nodding her thanks, she hurried to join Papa.

The weather did not look promising. Anxious to get home they left the friendly settlement, or yurt, as the small Tatar communities were called.

It was still bitterly cold. Even the layer of straw on the floor of the sleigh and the sheepskin lined leather boots did not keep Marie's feet from freezing.

"Are you all right?" asked Papa.

"Yes, Papa." She didn't want to complain. This trip with Papa had been a special treat and she didn't want to spoil it by whining. The further they traveled, the worse the weather became. Her hands were beginning to feel numb in her woolen lined fur gloves that usually kept her hands snug and warm.

The horses plunged forward into the gale force winds that blew directly into their faces. They knew they were going home and Papa just let them have their heads. As snow began falling, a full-blown blizzard made it impossible for the horses to see. Papa reluctantly turned the sleigh around and headed back for the Tatar village. For two more days, till the blizzard blew itself out, they remained with the gracious, friendly Tatars.

When they finally arrived home on Christmas Eve, a letter awaited Marie. It was from George Starodubzev, a school principal, asking her to come help in his office at Elancko Celo just seven miles from her home. She accepted. Part of her duties was to help a teacher who was teaching adults how to read and write. She also worked with the secretary and another young girl in the office.

Marie met another teacher, Valentina Pavlova, who, upon learning Marie was looking for a place to stay closer to the school, offered an extra room in her home. Marie was delighted and immediately moved in with her.

After the children left at the end of the day and Valentina's work was done, they would practice different songs in the empty classroom. Oh, how Marie loved to sing! After she had been at the school for several weeks, people began stopping by just to listen to them.

Marie had never been so happy. She liked the people and was having a wonderful time. She still thought that some day when the political chaos died down, she would like to travel. With Mr. Starodubzev's sponsorship, she obtained a passport that would permit her to visit foreign countries, for she was certain peace would not be long in coming.

In the spring, Valentina received a letter from Tyumen informing her that her father had died. She asked permission from the principal to close school sooner than planned. He agreed and Valentina left for Tyumen. Marie felt so lonely after she left. Mr. Starodubzev and his wife had a baby girl and asked Marie to be the baby's godmother. She was pleased, but she had decided to leave and return home.

Growing restless with country life, Marie went to Tyumen with her father. She was glad to be able to stay with Aunt Olga for by now refugees had flooded the town and living accommodations were impossible to find. She signed up for typing lessons and completed the course in two months.

While living in Tyumen, she met a young clerk in a bookstore and he became very attentive. He asked her out several times. She enjoyed being with him, but he began to get serious. When he asked her to marry him she told him she didn't know him well enough.

With her typing certificate in hand, she returned to Antipina. At nineteen she was feeling very restless. She knew some people were beginning to think of her as an old maid. Sister Anna was married with a baby and seemed happy though she never learned to read and write.

Marie stopped at the small room serving her sister as living quarters adjacent to a one-room shop. Barbara greeted Marie, "I have a problem. My supplies for the store have been cut off by the revolution and I do not know when I will be able to get any more merchandise from West Russia."

Barbara Ivanova had been sewing and selling clothes for a long time now. She had married, but her husband drank and spent all the money she made sewing. She divorced him, worked even harder and now owned her own little clothing store in Antipina.

"If you can't get more material I suppose you will have to close the shop," sympathized Marie as she poured herself some tea. "I have heard the Communists are getting closer."

"The only source of supplies for the store will have to come from Vladivostok, and in order to get there, a passport is required," worried Barbara. "It will take me too long to get a passport but I was wondering. You already have a passport. Would you go buy supplies for me?"

"Of course, I'll go," eagerly responded Marie. She had always wanted to travel. And now she could go to Vladivostok. She had only read about the city – and now she could actually go there!

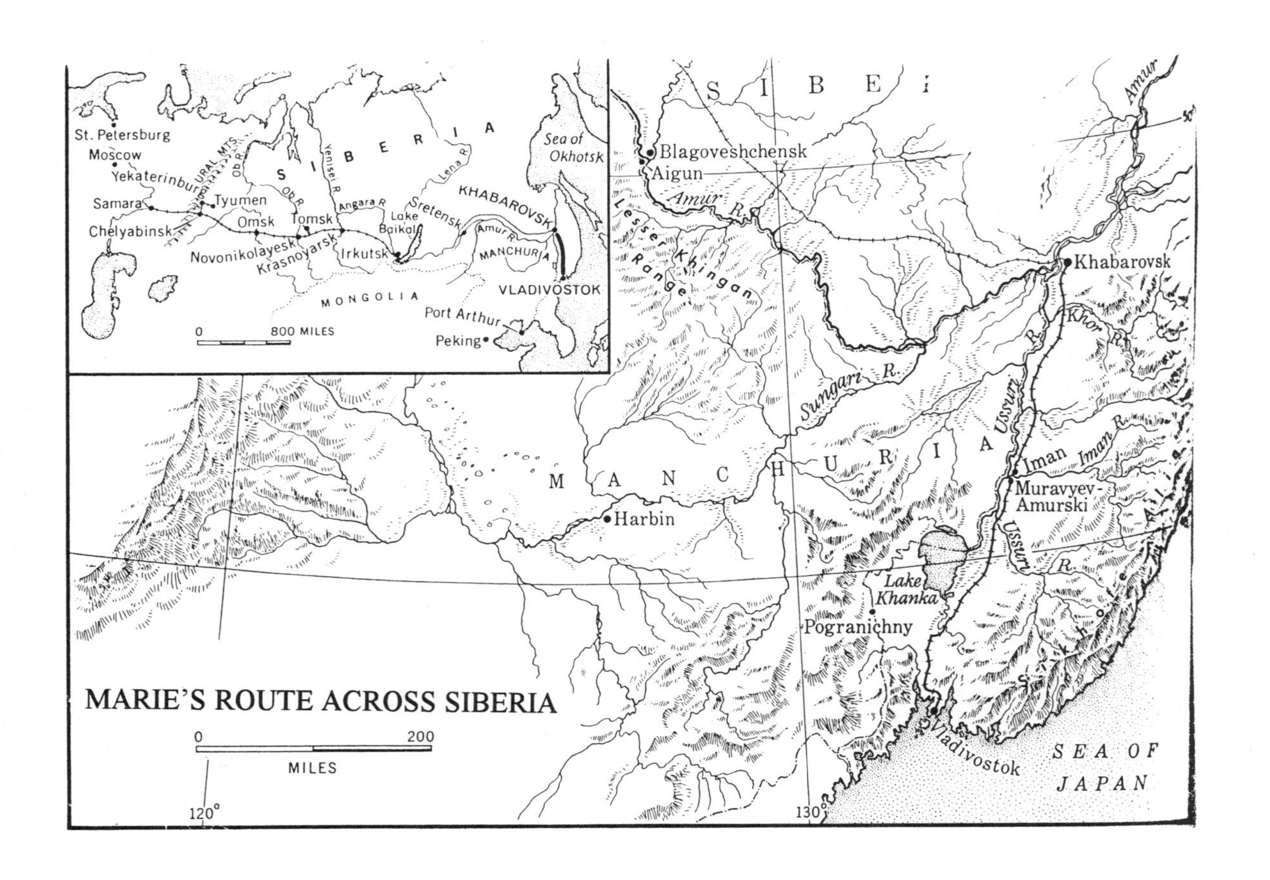
St. Petersburg
Moscow
Yekaterinburg
URAL MTS.
Samara
Chelyabinsk
Tyumen
Ob R.
Omsk
Novonikolayesk
Krasnoyarsk
Tomsk
S I B E R I A
Yenisei R.
Angara R.
Irkutsk
Lake Baikal
Sretensk
Lena R.
KHABAROVSK
Amur R.
MANCHURIA
VLADIVOSTOK
Sea of Okhotsk
MONGOLIA
Port Arthur
Peking
0
800 MILES
Blagoveshchensk
Aigun
Amur R.
Lesser Khingan Range
Amur
Khabarovsk
Khor R.
Sungari R.
Ussuri R.
Iman
Iman R.
Muravyev-Amurski
Ussuri R.
M A N C H U R I A
Harbin
Lake Khanka
Pogranichny
Vladivostok
SEA OF JAPAN
MARIE'S ROUTE ACROSS SIBERIA
0
200
MILES
120°
130°

CHAPTER EIGHT

BOARDING THE TRANS-SIBERIA RAILWAY

Marie was so excited. She actually was going to travel to Vladivostok. Barbara was paying for her trip. All she had to do was enjoy it, buy some things for Barbara, and return home.

Barbara cautioned, "I will give you money for travel and to buy supplies, but you will have to be very frugal about spending the money so you won't run out." She paused as she pondered, "Now, let's see. The trip is 4,400 miles and will take a full five days altogether. Then time to shop and look around a bit – you should be gone about two weeks. You can stay with my friends the Livingstons. I'll write a note to introduce you. Can you leave right away?"

"Just as soon as I get home to pack my clothes and ask Papa to drive me to the station," she was running to the door even as she spoke. She slowed, then shrugged aside a fleeting moment of trepidation recalling the train wreck just a few years ago.

She halted at the door as Barbara said seriously, "I will sew you a money belt while you're packing. You will be carrying (the equivalent of) two thousand dollars. No one must know you are carrying so much money or your life will be in danger."

Marie's mind raced as she tried to remember her geography. She thought of seeing Lake Baikal – and the Pacific Ocean – all the places she had dreamed about. She flew home to pack, ignoring the slight unease caused by Barbara's warning.

Marie gripped the handle of her wooden satchel, her blanket, and her cloth food bag. As she stood on the rough-hewn logs of the station platform of the Trans-Siberian railroad, the late July weather of 1919 was warm, and a slight breeze blew a loose strand of hair across her eyes. Standing there in her new traveling dress and her ankle-length velvet cape, she felt a little too hot, but she would need her heavy cape to keep her warm on her long journey.

"Goodbye, Papa, I will be back in a couple of weeks."

She turned and gave her father a hug, discreetly smoothing the slight bulge of her money belt. It nestled against her body in a snug fit, encircling her waist under her dress. At first it had felt uncomfortable, but she was getting used to the additional weight. She would not remove it until she reached Vladivostok.

Exhilaration filled Marie at the thought of the challenge ahead. She was actually going to Vladivostok! With her ticket safely inside her bag, she stepped to the door of the cattle wagon that would take her on her journey. A momentary longing caused her to turn around and wave to Papa. Raising his hand in reply, Papa smiled lovingly at his excited daughter.

Marie had learned how to trade and barter from watching Papa day after day and now she was going to do some bartering on her own for her sister's materials. "I do hope I can be as good a trader as Papa," she thought to herself.

Glancing at the sign posted on the side of the cattle wagon she read, "Capacity 13 horses or 43 men." Climbing the steps to the double door, she peered into the dimly lit car. It took a few seconds for her eyes to adjust from the sunlight outside. Boards were nailed down the middle of the floor to create a sort of aisle space for walking. Shelves hammered into the walls of the car provided the only seats. She looked around trying to locate an empty shelf that she could claim as her own for the next five days.

Spotting a vacant spot towards the back of the car, she stepped

Box-cars on the Trans-Siberian Railway at the time Marie made her trip.

over the legs of a sleeping child lying on the floor of the crowded car. The stench of unwashed, sweaty bodies assailed her nose and she involuntarily covered her face with her hand. The car was filled with fleeing refugees, peasants, and soldiers with a variety of different uniforms, making it impossible to identify their units.

Stowing her bag underneath the grimy, uncushioned seat, she frowned as she sat down on her folded blanket, deciding it would probably be a lot dirtier before she got to Vladivostok anyway.

The acrid smell of cow and horse manure left no doubt in Marie's mind that the car had been used to carry livestock before being pressed into service as a passenger wagon. All the passenger and luxury cars for the nobility had long since been removed to Western Russia during the war. The smell reminded her of shoveling out the barns at home in the spring. This was going to be a long five days.

To think Barbara had to pay extra for these squalid accommodations. Due to the tremendous demand for space on the train, caused by the revolution, Barbara had been forced to bribe officials in order to get a ticket.

An exhausted mother with three children sat next to Marie and an elderly man with a long white beard sat on the other side. The tired faces of the children indicated they had been traveling for quite some time.

Marie asked the well-dressed, but much rumpled woman, "How long have you been traveling?"

She looked at Marie with haunted eyes. "We have been running from the Communists for three weeks, but on the train for two days. They captured and murdered my husband." The anger and bitterness too deep for tears, shot the words out almost like the firing of a pistol. She sadly continued, "The children and I have been hiding out and running for our lives ever since."

Horror engulfed Marie. The impact of the revolution finally penetrated. A tremendous inconvenience had become a terrifying reality.

Belching smoke and hissing steam from the big locomotive interrupted them as Marie felt the slight movement of the car. When the big engine picked up speed, the iron wheels began to vibrate and clatter on the widely spaced iron rails.

She was on her way.

There were no windows, but through the opened upper sections of the double doors, Marie could see into the distance. Farms nestled on the plains as the train rolled by. How peaceful the green fields and pastures dotted with cattle and horses seemed in contrast to the turmoil written on the faces of her traveling companions.

Before long, Marie needed to find the restroom. The woman beside her informed her that the facility was in an adjoining car. It consisted of a small closet with a toilet and tiny wash basin, with very little water available. Both sexes shared this reeking facility and a long wait in line was uncomfortable, wearisome, and sometimes, embarrassing.

A trip on the Trans-Siberian railroad had never been smooth even in the luxurious first-class accommodations. Here again were soft rails (each weighing only 49 pounds per foot as compared to those of England's 60 pounds and those of The United States at 90 pounds) with widely spaced ties and poorly compacted fill. In addition the trains ran on Petersburg time, and indifferent time schedules.

Stations were frequently a mile or more away from the cities along the route. It was alleged that when the Czar planned the railroad, he laid a ruler across the nation, irregardless of terrain or urban areas. Whether true or not, the railroad definitely was not designed for the convenience of the local inhabitants.

Marie leaned back against the swaying wall of the car and closed her eyes. Before long, the rhythmic clacking of the iron wheels slowed. The clanging of a bell signaled the train's approach to another station. A hissing white cloud of steam billowed forth from the engine as it rolled to a halt.

A very few passengers got off. Marie was amazed at the number of people who were trying to force their way into the packed cattle cars. The woman beside her told her that they were White refugees trying to get away from West Russia. Marie had never seen so many desperate looking faces. Crowds jammed the space around the station, begging and pleading to get on the train. As the train pulled away, many tried to grasp hold of the outside of the car. Marie was unaware that people were actually being trampled to death fighting for a chance to escape the oncoming Communist menace.

The shelf-like bench was very hard and uncomfortable. Marie tried to sleep in the small space she was allotted, but there was not enough room to stretch out. She tried sleeping in a fetal position using her coat for a pillow and her blanket for covering. During the first night on the train, she was awakened when a small, soft, furry body brushed against her leg. A rat was trying to steal from her food bag. After that night she held the sack within the curve of her body so she could fight off the rats. In the dim light, their beady eyes, long whiskers and long tails appeared wicked and menacing. She wondered where they disappeared to in the daytime.

At this time of year in July, dawn came early and dusk came late, which was a blessing for the only lighting at night was supplied by candles.

As Marie opened her food bag and tore off a chunk of bread, she realized that her food wasn't going to last the entire trip. Already they had made several unscheduled stops due to craters in the roadbed sometimes caused by sabotage with handmade bombs, or sections of track pulled loose by horses. Robbery had probably been the intent, but the number of soldiers on board may have discouraged the would-be thieves. It took hours to repair damages before they could continue their journey.

On the taiga the land was bare of trees except for small birches and willows too small to be of any use except for firewood. Only a few hardy people lived here, and most of them survived by providing food for the railroad. When the train stopped to pick up firewood to fuel the giant engine, peasant women sold their eggs, bread, cheese, milk, fruit, vegetables or whatever they had, to the passengers. Some of them baked anything from big loaves of bread to small rolls and a few even had cakes to sell. At one stop, Marie stepped out of the car to replenish her food supply.

Armed guards at the stations, flanked by blockhouses, protected

Accidents along the Trans-Siberian Railway were common at the time Marie made her trip.

the train from the hordes of refugees trying to board the train. Marie quickly bought rolls and cheese from the closest vendors and returned to the train. Only ticketed passengers were allowed back aboard. The press of the hopeful travelers frightened her.

Marie was relieved to once again be underway, but to her discomfort, she found another source of irritation. Mosquitoes were so thick that everyone suffered from the thirsty, pesky insects. The wide excavations on both sides of the track running through the taiga, collected rain and melting perma-frost moisture that provided a home for millions of mosquitoes. They got into the cars too, but the haze from the cigarettes and pipe smoke helped to keep the numbers down.

Marie was shocked by the multitude of refugees walking along the tracks, and she was appalled by the countless number of bodies lying in the ditches along the rails, that could not be buried because of the frozen sub-soil. Some were wrapped in blankets, but most were in various degrees of decomposition. Flies swarmed and maggots consumed the rotting flesh. Birds of prey fought over morsels of flesh torn from the putrefying bodies. She had never seen anything so horrible. Why had all these people died?

In order to keep from thinking about the grisly sights and to forget the miserable conditions on the train, Marie began to sing. Singing helped to ease her tension and pass the time. The three children nearby watched and listened to her, wide-eyed and occasionally smiling when she sang a joyful song. This pleased Marie.

Marie lay dozing on her bench with her legs hanging over the side and the food sack held tightly in her arms. Suddenly, the sound of an explosion startled her awake. The lurching of the car as the engineer stopped the train, sent her reeling off the shelf. Bumping into the old man next to her, she scrambled to her feet. The screeching of the iron wheels, combined with the slamming of the cars as they jammed into the car ahead, panicked Marie.

"The train must be wrecking," Marie instantly recalled another train wreck as she was knocked off her feet. Catching herself before she fell flat, she shakily stood up in the now immobile car. The children were crying. Everyone was shaken, but thankfully, no one was hurt.

The two guards who were walking ahead of the train to check the tracks had failed to spot a barricade in time to prevent an abrupt halt. The planted explosive was detected and detonated; the crater must be filled and track restored. Marauders had struck again.

The train was now in the thick timber of spruce, larch, pine, and

A view of German prisoners of war at work on the Trans-Siberian Railway in 1917.

birch, which provided good cover for renegade bands. The trees were so dense here that the sun never reached the forest floor. The conductor said that sixty below zero in the winter was not unusual.

Now wide awake, all the passengers talked to dispel their nervousness. Marie listened intently to a woman telling someone next to her of an experience while traveling the previous year.

"We heard shouting and gunfire towards the front of the train. Shortly after we stopped, several armed men surrounded us shouting, 'Everyone off the train! We want your money, any jewelry, and any other valuables you are carrying.'

"I was petrified! I had a little cash in my purse, but I had sewed money into the hem of my skirt. We were lined up along the car while some ransacked the luggage, and two ragged ruffians held a gun on us, and others pawed our bodies. Just as I was sure my money would be found, the searcher's attention was caught by a gun shot. Another looter had met resistance. An old man had a watch he valued and he tried to grab it back when it was taken from him. They shot him in the head and shouted at us. 'You'll get the same if you don't cooperate!' We cooperated."

"And, do you know, the conductor just shoved the body further into the ditch and the train went on just like nothing had happened. Do you suppose it happens so often they think nothing of it?"

Marie thought of Barbara's money strapped around her waist. To reassure herself she hugged her arms tightly against her body as Barbara's words of warning came back to her.

"Where do the bandits come from?" Marie asked the old man sitting beside her.

"They could be escaped convicts, White defectors, Red partisans, vagrant soldiers, or just local peasants. These are hard times and there is much unrest these days; many people have resorted to stealing in order to live. No one is safe any more."

Bending over to pick up his coat, he neatly folded it and set it on the bench. Then he went on, "The Trans-Siberian Railroad is the only link between East and West Russia, and all supplies have to travel over these rails. Passengers and shipments of goods are at the mercy of bands of thieves. There are not enough soldiers to make the line safe."

Listening intently to the old man, Marie was overcome with a yearning for her family. To ward off loneliness, Marie began singing in a low voice, an old Russian folk song. Heads turned as the passengers strained to hear her sweet, melodious voice. Pleasure in singing overcame her shyness and she sang more loudly and with confidence.

Toes tapped and bodies swayed as all relaxed from their harrowing experience and became enthralled with the music. The light airy tunes mesmerized the tired travelers. Written on the faces surrounding her was a dreamlike aura that bespoke of recollections of a happier time. It felt good to be singing again, thought Marie, as she too was carried back to memories of family gatherings around the fire. The melodies she loved to sing flowed easily from her lips.

A smile crossed the old man's face. Leaning back against the wall, he closed his eyes and rocked his head from side to side in time with the music. Some of the passengers started humming along. Soon the humming turned to singing. Before long, many of the people were singing along with Marie, drawn together with a common bond; the music helped pass the time. When the singing stopped, the travelers began to visit. Up until then, everyone had kept to himself, not trusting the person next him. The singing seemed to help everyone feel better.

Finally, the whistle blew; the track was repaired. The passengers who had been outside, clambered up into the car. Creaking and groaning the train slowly picked up speed. It had taken five hours to remove the barricade and fill the hole made by the explosive. In these dense woods, rock and dirt for fill were not easy to get.

Quiet settled over the weary passengers, but Marie was unable to sleep. Unashamedly eavesdropping, she listened as the old man softly, lest he awakened those sleeping, told his neighbor about the building of the Trans-Siberian Railroad.

The Czar had mandated a railroad be built across all Siberia to link Western Russia with Vladivostok on the Pacific coast. Nicholas II laid the first stone in 1891 when construction started northward from Vladivostok. Simultaneously, building began from Chelyabinsk, the connection to the railroad network in European Russia. The Czar was in hopes that the railroad would give him better control of his empire, that it would encourage settlement of sparsely populated Siberia, and also help bridge the cultural gap between Siberia and Western Russia.

The 4,050 miles of new line was completed in 1904. The longest railroad in the world did not come easy – swamps, numerous wide rivers, steep grades, high mountains, permafrost, temperature extremes, disease, insects – all plagued the motley crews made up of local labor, soldiers, Chinese coolies, other foreigners, and laborers recruited from West Russia, some of whom brought their families and remained to help settle Siberia. Winter weather restricted the building to only four months a year. Digging the numerous tunnels could continue through the winter, if the workers could withstand the bitter weather outside. Twice as many supplies could be hauled in the winter by sled than in the summer by river boat.

The tunnels and bridges were designed to allow for two sets of tracks, but only one track was laid and that of a wider gauge than used throughout the rest of the world, intended to be a handicap for foreign invaders. Some bridges had from one to five main spans as long as three hundred fifty feet each. The term "hogback" arose from comparing the rise in the middle of each span to the profile of a pig's back.

In 1896, a treaty had been signed with China, granting permission for the line to pass through northern Manchuria. The grant gave some control over the province in the north as well. The Chinese also leased Liaotung Peninsula to the Russians where they established Port Arthur, the finest natural port along the Pacific coast, and Port Darien.

Russia's treaty with China did not please Japan who had been settling their people in Korea and Manchuria. The Japanese did, in fact, own the Korean railroad and were in control of the economy and trade of Korea.

Russia did not abide by her treaty with China. This gave the Japanese an excuse to declare war in 1904. Japan was prepared for war.

The government had insisted upon their people becoming educated as rapidly as possible, enabling them to adapt to all the latest available technology to prepare for war. Russia was totally unprepared.

Attacking the Russian ships anchored at Port Arthur, Japan immobilized the fleet and demoralized the military personnel. The Czar belatedly sent his prize fleet, stationed in the Baltic, out through the North Sea and Straits of Dover, down the coast of Africa, and around the point of Madagascar. They continued on across the Indian Ocean into the Pacific and South China Seas. The fleet consisted of eight battleships, twelve cruisers, and nine destroyers.

On May 27, 1904, at Togo, the Japanese fleet, equipped with about the same number of boats – only faster – intercepted the Russian fleet. Within an hour, Russia's fleet had been reduced to one cruiser and one destroyer which escaped and limped to Vladivostok. Though the Trans-Siberian railroad was completed through Manchuria by that time, supplies were not getting through. Japan had pulled 180,000 troops from Korea and had 30,000 more waiting to strike.

Back at Petersburg nobody was very interested in Japan. There were some who were busy plotting the overthrow of the Czar; many who did not favor war. The people were just too concerned with their own problems to worry over a small bunch of islands in the Pacific. When the Japanese Ambassador came to see the Czar, Nicholas was too busy hunting pheasants to see him.

Japan completely routed the Russian army of 80,000 troops, incompetently lead. A peace treaty was signed at Mukden in 1905, forcing Russia to give up Port Arthur and Port Darien, the southern portion of Sakhalin Island, to abandon any interest in Korea, as well as give up any portion of the Trans-Siberian Railroad that was located within Manchuria's borders.

The old man rubbed his eyes and shook his head. "The new section of line was just completed four years ago from Kuenga to Vladivostok, adding almost 500 miles more to the trip. But at least travelers no longer need a passport to get through Manchuria.

Marie's ears perked up. One of the reasons she was making this trip instead of Barbara was that she had a passport.

The old man continued on.

"Now that the railroad line has been laid around the south end of Lake Baikal, it is easier to complete the trip. At first, in order to cross the forty mile width of the lake in summer, they had to load the trains onto the deck of the ferry and portage across. The ferry was 290 feet long, 57 feet across the beam and drew 20 feet of water. Three pairs of tracks lay parallel with the keel. They could accommodate between 25 to 28 fully loaded cars, as well as coaches. Fog often interfered. The chill water of Baikal in contrast to the summer heat caused a fog that might delay traffic for days. In winter they would lay the tracks across the thick ice of Lake Baikal and run the trains across the lake until the ice became too thin in the spring."

"How do you know so much about the railroad?" asked the bearded man.

"I am a professor of engineering at the University of Tomsk," he answered. "I am heading home. I will be taking the spur line to Tomsk tomorrow. You know, it is said that the people of Tomsk refused to pay the engineers the $50,000 they asked to plan the railroad through Tomsk rather than Omsk. Actually, the land is so swampy and forested that it took one year to build the spur and another half year to improve it so it was usable."

Turning to his neighbor, he asked, "Where are you going?"

The bearded man looked furtively around the cattle car. "I am getting away from the Communists." He nervously pulled at his beard as he looked around again. "I have seen them do things – commit such atrocities. No one will be safe if they win."

The train rumbled down the track. Night had fallen and the candles cast dim light throughout the car. Marie thought about all she had heard. Russia was such a big country and she realized she had seen such a small part of it. She had wanted to travel and here she was riding the longest railroad in the world. She hadn't expected the trip to take so long. She had lost track of how many days they were behind schedule.

CHAPTER NINE

A RUSSIAN SOLDIER MAKES A TEDIOUS TRIP BEARABLE

Marie looked forward to seeing Omsk. She had heard that the city was larger than any she had seen so far, that it was a rail and river boat center, and that the temperature ranged from ninety degrees in the summer to an average of forty-two degrees below zero in the winter. When the train arrived at the station early in the morning, she was disappointed. She was to learn that the main urban area was a mile away.

A few of the passengers, including the professor, got off here. The station was bustling with soldiers; in fact, it looked like a military depot. Upon inquiry, she was told Omsk was the headquarters for the White Army in Siberia.

Looking up and down the rough-planked station platform, she observed the solid-looking white brick and block depot. The smoke from train engines had turned the white bricks a shade of gray. Roman arches decorated the tops of the doorways and windows on all the buildings facing the train. Decorative facades helped Marie distinguish where one building ended and another began. Buildings here were much more ornate than in her hometown of Antipina.

Lining the station platform were hopeful families huddled together with their meager possessions, waiting for space on the train. Buckets and baskets stacked along with spinning wheels, cooking utensils, and the indispensable samovar, were piled beside the weary travelers. Beggars with hands extended asked new arrivals for hand-outs. Basket peddlers were chanting their sales pitch to anyone who would listen.

Down past the station on the rail sidings, there were rail cars in which thousands of refugees, emaciated and sickly, were living. With no funds to travel and little hope for change, they subsisted mainly on black bread and tea. From their plight came the dubbing of Omsk as the "city of the living dead." Marie felt almost guilty because there was nothing she could do to ease their plight.

Her growling stomach reminded her that the supply of food in her bag was getting low. Climbing down from the cattle car, she made her way over to a vender who was selling biscuits, meat, and cheeses. After eating her breakfast, she carried her purchases back to the train. With her arms full, she accidently dropped one of her packages. Before she could bend over to pick it up, a uniformed soldier retrieved it for her.

"I believe this is yours," he said as he winced slightly handing her the package. His blue eyes, the color of the sky, looked tired, and his face seemed a little pale. Smiling at her, he stated, "It looks like we are going to be traveling companions."

"Thank you," she replied as she tipped her head slightly so he could not see the blush creeping into her cheeks.

Abruptly turning and boarding the car, she felt her heart beating just a little faster. The soldier was handsome, she thought as she put her packages into her food bag and replaced it under the bench. Turning sharply, she nearly unbalanced the new passenger who was storing away his bags. She could only see his back.

Her mind still on the kind, good-looking soldier who had picked up her package, she reclaimed her portion of the bench and sat down. With eyes downcast, she checked to make sure she had replaced her ticket.

"What a coincidence," said a deep husky voice Marie had heard before.

Quickly glancing up, Marie stared into the bright blue eyes of the attractive man she had been thinking about.

"May I sit beside you? This appears to be the only vacant seat in this car."

"Of course," Marie replied as she reached up to brush back a loose strand of hair away from her eyes. Marie knew that she must look rumpled. It had been at least twenty-four hours since she had braided her chestnut-colored hair and wrapped it in a circle around her head. She furtively tried to smooth out the wrinkles in her skirt. As her hand brushed against the money belt, she immediately became more alert. No one must know she was carrying a large sum of money or she would be in danger.

"I am Nikolai Zukov. I am an officer in the Russian army," he informed her as he slightly bowed and clicked his heels together. She recognized the uniform as that of the Czar's military.

"I am Marie Zimina," she responded as she shook his extended hand.

Sitting down, he winced. Marie looked concerned, "Are you all right?"

"Yes, I am fine now. I am just a little stiff from an injury. I have been in the hospital and I am being reassigned at Irkutsk."

The train whistle blew loudly and the hissing of the steam was drowned out by the clanging of the wheels as the train pulled away from the station. Many people, who were unable to buy tickets because the train was full, stood forlornly watching as the train picked up speed.

Marie and Nikolai visited while the train slowly proceeded down the hurriedly repaired track. Marie told him she was going to visit in Vladivostok, but said nothing about shopping or the money she was carrying. She did not want him to know.

Nikolai Zukov.

Before long, the train stopped so that fallen trees could be cleared from the track. There were no trees immediately adjoining the tracks, so obviously these had been placed to form a barricade. Great caution was necessary. Guards were immediately posted along the track, preparing for a possible ambush.

The passengers begged Marie to sing. She started the songs and before long, almost everyone was joining with her. The time passed quickly.

Nikolai appeared surprised and enthralled by Marie's beautiful voice. He sat back on his bench and watched her while she sang and clapped her hands in time with the music. His obvious admiration thrilled her and she sang song after song with others occasionally chiming in until the track was safely cleared. Evidently the sight of the guards had thwarted any attack.

"You appear so happy when you sing. Happiness is rare these days." Nikolai complimented her.

"I love to sing," she stated simply, then asked. "Why are you so sad? And you are obviously in pain. Would I be rude if I asked you what is wrong?"

Nikolai responded, "Not at all. I am flattered that you are interested enough to ask. But it's a long story."

Marie said nothing but waited for him to continue.

"For so long my life has been in turmoil, it is hard for me to remember happy days. I lost my family years ago from plague and I lied about my age to get into the army,"

Pausing thoughtfully a moment he continued, "I guess I am lucky to be alive. My unit was assigned to a troop train. I am the only one left. The Reds had set fire to the bridge ahead of us. When the engineer reversed, trying to go back, the bridge behind was burning as well. I climbed to the top of a car to get a better shot at the attackers. I was shot in the arm. I fell, bumping my head. I was knocked unconscious." He paused obviously reliving his experience.

Marie noted his wincing at the pain as he rubbed his throbbing arm.

"When I revived, there were only dead bodies around me. I had been stripped of any valuables – even my boots," he added ruefully. "I guess they thought I was dead."

"I'm not sure how long I lay there before repair crews found me and took me to the hospital at Omsk." He paused, "Now all I want is to get this crazy war over so I can get on with my studies. But for now I am being reassigned at Irkutsk where I will help to keep the railroad open. I suppose I will be working mostly with Czech soldiers."

Marie had heard that Czechoslovakian soldiers had defected to Russia to avoid conscription in Austrian-Hungarian forces during the war. They came well-armed, and sided with Russia against Germany. The abrupt ending of the war, brought about by the Bolshevik's separate peace with Germany, left them stranded with the German army between them and home. They agreed to give up their arms in order to be sent on the Trans-Siberian Railroad to Vladivostok, where, hopefully, they could sail for France, who had agreed to let them pass through to their homeland.

In Vladivostok, no passage had been available. They had thrown in with the Whites who offered to pay them to guard the railroad between Omsk and Lake Baikal. They were stationed along the fifteen hundred mile stretch. When lacking sufficient man-power to guard bridges, tunnels and longer distances of track, they recruited the local peasants. If the local peasants did not warn of saboteurs, the Czech soldiers burned the peasants' villages.

"Someone should have been guarding the bridges that were set afire, trapping us," said Nikolai. "I'll probably never know exactly what happened. Many good soldiers lost their lives due to someone's carelessness. There is much distrust between the Czechs and the peasants, and the peasants turn on the Czechs at any opportunity."

"It's hard to place the blame. Everyone's nerves are at the breaking point." He went on to explain.

"Captured Hungarian prisoners are being detained in Siberia. A Hungarian threw a piece of iron at a Czech soldier who immediately shot him. As punishment, several Czech soldiers were imprisoned by the White army. Armed Czechs demanded the prisoners be released and, demands not met, proceeded to release the prisoners themselves. An edict followed that any Czech soldier found carrying arms shall be shot. The Czechs never have received their promised pay. They started smuggling guns and fending for themselves, and are now joining in the pillaging."

(The last Czech evacuated was in 1920.)

By now, most soldiers of all groups were in rags, carrying their arms and supplies in potato sacks. Reds, Whites, Czechs, partisans, and locals were all equally vicious. Nikolai could not understand why the White administration at Omsk had done nothing. If a few of the military offenders had been disciplined or shot when caught, some chaos might have been averted. However, Kolchak, the White commander at Omsk, remained completely out of touch with the people. His headquarters teemed with hundreds of White Russian officers currying favors and supposedly in charge of the 5,000 soldiers who were prepared to do anything but fight.

The peasants had suffered greatly from the Whites by forced imprisonment. Villages had been burned, individuals were shot, hanged, or dropped alive through holes in the ice. The war was pitting neighbor against neighbor and no one could come out the winner. Trotsky was advancing further and further along the railroad line. Partisans, repulsed by the cruelty of the Whites, aided the Reds who were just as vicious towards any who tried to resist them.

Nikolai sighed. "Where is it all going to end? Here I sit beside a beautiful girl who sings like a canary. I've no idea what the future holds, but I would like to get to know you better. Your singing has made me happy for the first time in a long time."

Nodding his head, eyes closed, sleep overcame the tired soldier.

Marie watched Nikolai as he slept. What made him frown in his sleep? He had moaned once or twice when he moved. Obviously, his wound still pained him. In just a few short hours they had become friends. They had talked about their families and the villages where they had been raised. She shared some of her food with him and he had shared his with her. Marie had never felt this way about a man before. She liked Nikolai.

Now nearly twenty, Marie knew she was considered an old maid, but she had never met a man like Nikolai. He was interesting to talk to, they shared many common interests, and he loved to hear her sing.

Traveling through the steppes, they saw the lush gardens of the farmers. The fields of grain seemed to come alive as the wind rippled and swirled, bowing and swaying the unending prairie of ripening grain. Soon the green would turn to brown. Summers were so short. She thought that they really had two seasons – winter and summer. It was said that one must be sharp or he would miss the one day that spring and fall each occurred.

Marie and Nikolai laughed and sang to forget the tedious ride.

Everybody was so tired of the delays. By now Marie had expected to be in Vladivostok, but she still hadn't reached Lake Baikal. When she mentioned this to Nikolai he said, "I am glad the train has gone slow. It has given me a chance to spend more time with you. I must get off at Irkutsk."

He was right. As soon as they reached Irkutsk, he would be gone, and she would still have several days' journey ahead. She became sad at the thought of his leaving. They had become very good friends.

Nikolai noted her sadness and, trying to cheer her, he said, "You will enjoy seeing Lake Baikal. The lake is the most beautiful blue, like your eyes. It is four hundred miles long and forty to seventy miles wide. I have heard that is it over a mile deep in places. There are many seals that live in the lake. The railroad skirts the southern shoreline. The Russian Geographical Society at Irkutsk has identified over one thousand plant and animal species unique to the area. Maybe, if your are lucky, you can see some seals on the shoreline."

Marie knew he was trying to avoid the subject of their parting, but she was glad he was sharing that information with her because, next to singing, learning was her favorite thing to do.

Nikolai continued, "There are mountain ranges on both sides of Lake Baikal. I've heard it said that one-tenth of the earth's fresh water is in Baikal. There are three hundred rivers that empty into the Lake, but only one that flows out. You can see a white stone at the bottom of the lake in water one hundred twenty feet deep, the water is so clear."

Marie's heart raced as he reached over and gently covered her hand with his. Holding her hand, he turned to her and whispered, "Marie Zimina, I would so very much like to take you for a walk through the forest of trees on stilts on Pachannaya Bay on Lake Baikal."

Scene of the trans-Siberian Railway along the Baikal Mountain section.

He sighed as he held her hand up to his cheek. "You would enjoy seeing the pine and larch trees elevated high enough in the air by their roots that we could walk under them between the roots. This phenomenon occurs because the wind blows the sand out from under the tree roots and they just keep growing downward to support the tree."

His eyes brightened. "Maybe you could stop on your way back home and I can show you the miracles of Lake Baikal."

Slumping back against the cattle car, he shook his head. "What am I saying, I don't even know where I am going to be in a couple of weeks."

Marie squeezed his hand and smiled at him. "Maybe some day you can take me on that tour."

It was sweet of Nikolai to try to divert her, but how Marie wished she could take a bath and wash her hair. After so many days on the train and only enough water in the restroom to do no more than wash her hands, she felt grubby. She would have liked to fix up a little for Nikolai. She had never felt this way about a man before. She just knew that before the trip was over she would get lousy; people were packed close, and many were scratching from lice.

At times it seemed that they were the only two in the cattle car as they talked and laughed. Each time their arms brushed, Marie felt her heart lurch and beat faster.

As the train was stopping, Nikolai took her hand in his and looking into her eyes, said, "Marie, I want to keep in touch with you. Please write to me. Here is my military address. I want you to know that you have brought a little sunshine into this soldier's life. Your music made me very happy. Thank you." He kissed her hand and laid it against his cheek again. "I will always remember you, Marie Zimina."

The train stopped. Nikolai picked up his bag and walked off the train. Turning, he smiled and waved, but his eyes were sad. Tears welled up in Marie's eyes. She had only known him for a few days, but she had grown fond of the handsome Russian soldier. As she watched him disappear into the throng surrounding the cattle car, she felt like a part of her was going with him. She stood, bereft and lonely now that he was gone.

With her journey only half completed, Marie knew she must purchase food for the remainder of the trip. She had only planned for five days and already she had spent eleven – or was it twelve? – days, to get halfway. Time had ceased to register. Only discomfort, lice, filth, and lack of sleep were real.

Irkutsk was an old city, founded by the Cossacks in 1661. The main city was across the bridge over the Angara River. It was also a modern city with a theater and museum.

At the station, crowded together with the soldiers, were men and women from many cultures, mingling and bustling. They reminded Marie of bees swarming around a hive. There were Tatars, who were Islams of Turkish descent and dressed in their colorful clothes; assertive bearded Cossacks with their high leather boots styled for riding; a mustached, bearded, turbaned Kirgiz chief with his hooded falcon sitting on his outstretched arm and secured by leather thongs attached to the falcons legs; Buryats with their colorful belts and cone-shaped fur hats; along with many Russian peasants dressed in high boots, sheepskin outer clothes, and fur caps. There were many others whose culture Marie could not readily identify.

Many languages Marie could not understand clamored in her ears. She felt lost and alone in this seething mass of humanity. The melting pot of ethnic groups reminded her of her favorite stew with all the vegetables cooked together in the same pot, but each vegetable retaining its flavor and color.

She realized that passengers were hurrying to purchase food, and she had better join them. The train was only scheduled to stop for twenty minutes at each station. Not that they often met that schedule, but she dared not risk the chance that this time they might.

She hastily made her purchases of Dutch cheese, wild strawberries and cream, and a couple of loaves of black bread that were about two inches in diameter and a foot long. Returning to the cattle car, she paused, looking in the direction in which Nikolai had disappeared. Sadly, she returned to her bench and put away the food.

With the blowing of the whistle, the train slowly pulled out of the station. Marie could see the many cars and engines parked in the train yard as they gradually picked up speed. Two men, standing in the open sectional doorway, pointed to a camel caravan heading into town, loaded with bales of tea from China. But it passed before Marie and others could see.

At one time, the camel and horse were the only means of transportation from China and Mongolia to Russia. Once the railroad was built, the need for camel caravans diminished, but in some areas they were still necessary to transport goods and people from isolated regions. Marie was disappointed; she had read about such things in her studies. She wished she had looked in time – she had never seen a camel.

As the train approached Lake Baikal, Marie could see the mountains in the distance that Nikolai had told her about. The huge, sparkling lake was every bit as beautiful as he had said. Wistfully, she thought of the short time they had spent together and wondered if she would ever see him again. She had left a little of her heart with Nikolai. She would never tell anyone, but she would keep his memory locked inside her heart forever.

They were entering steep mountain country covered with forests of pine and spruce. The Yablonovy Mountains were precipitous; the steep grades slowed the train. In one forty-four mile stretch of railroad, the passengers counted eighty-two bridges. The line was curvy and the embankments very narrow. Even though it was July, an occasional avalanche closed the line. While the snow was almost gone, mud slides caused by heavy rain or tremors from the numerous earthquakes, occurred. As many as two thousand quakes a year had been recorded in this area.

Shoveling the track clear took time. Marie would start singing to cheer the exhausted passengers who usually joined in. She filled many hours crocheting. By now she and the others felt much safer. Being closer to Vladivostok, the fighting was behind them.

The new section of railroad swung north of Mongolia and China, built far enough from the banks of the Amur River that shots fired from the border could not reach the train. This was the habitat of the Manchurian tiger, the largest in the world. Marie hoped she would see one, but the wily animals had not survived by making public appearances.

Swinging south through the Ussuri river valley there were several scheduled, but few unscheduled, stops. Farms flourished in the foothills and flatland in the valley. Many Japanese had moved into this area under the pretext of protecting the natives from the Czech soldiers; some had become proficient farmers, but more remained soldiers on duty.

Sixteen days after Marie had left Tyumen, the train pulled into Vladivostok. While she had always wanted to travel, she had not expected the stark accommodations, the filth, and the horrors she had seen. But, she had made it. Barbara's money was secure. After so much sitting, it was good to be able to stretch and walk, knowing she wouldn't have to get back on the crowded cattle car for at least ten days.

CHAPTER TEN

VLADIVOSTOK

Standing on the station platform, Marie looked around. So this was Vladivostok. The brick and block station with its ornate arches was somewhat larger than the others along the line. The train smoke blended with a slightly salty fishy smell, though she could not identify the source.

She looked at the address of Barbara's friends, the Livingstons. Immediately, she approached the ticket window inside the station and asked for directions. Tired, disheveled, and desperate for a bath, Marie trudged into town. Her bag grew heavier and heavier. In spite of fatigue, she remained ever alert to potential danger should someone realize she was carrying what she considered a large sum of money.

The directions had been specific. Marie introduced herself and Mrs. Livingston seemed very pleased to meet her. Realizing Marie was exhausted, without hesitation her gracious hostess insisted she rest and perhaps Marie would like a good soak first. They could visit after Marie rested. Marie needed no coaxing.

For the first time in sixteen days Marie removed the money belt, but placed it on a stool near the tub so she could keep an eye on it. She basked in the luxury of the warm water. Stretching, she sank into the soothing, cleansing, relaxing bath. Soaking sixteen days of grime, sweat, and soot off her body felt so good. Luxuriating in the tub, she closed her eyes and thought about Nikolai. Would she ever see him again? The cooling water finally roused her and she washed her hair.

Carrying only a part of her money with her each time, she set about purchasing all that she could for Barbara's store. Because each shipment was limited to ten pounds per person, she could ship home only fifty pounds, naming the adults in her family as recipients. She enjoyed dealing and shopping in the two large department stores in Vladivostok which had a wide variety of items and no rationing. Because she could read and write, she was able to get the best buys for her sister. Papa would be proud of the way she bargained for all the materials.

Before she spent too much, she must make provision for getting the merchandise to Antipina. Shipping on the railroad had become a con game with merchants forced to pay exorbitant prices for freight. Empty freight cars suddenly became available if sufficient palms were crossed with money. If extra money was not paid, engineers might fail to deliver merchandise promptly. Goods might or might not reach their destination. Conductors, brakemen, or even engineers who were all poorly paid, and sometimes paid no wages at all, might sell freight along the many stops they made. Marauding bands often confiscated shipments. But Marie was unaware of all these problems as she paid what they asked to mail her packages.

Along with the merchandise, she sent a letter home and one to Nikolai.

Now, she would see more of Vladivostok; the Livingstons were more than happy to have her with them and she felt at home with them.

Marie never tired of watching the ocean. Vladivostok was built on the edge of a deep natural harbor within a cove that was protected from the waves of the deep ocean. During the winter, the port froze over for three or four months until spring thaw. The town itself was built on gently rolling hills overlooking the bustling harbor. Fish canneries lined the waterfront permeating the whole town with the smell of rotten fish.

A photograph of what was known as the "Thieves Market" in the city of Vladivostok at the time Marie was there.

Shipbuilding yards were interspersed with the canneries and piers. A cacophony of sounds drifted up from the harbor day and night. The harbor was crowded with vessels from all over the world: sampans from china, dambes from Japan, motorized ships from America, and cutters from the north, vied for space at the docks. The hustle and the bustle of the docks fascinated Marie.

A main avenue ran the entire length of the city winding and twisting its way along the harbor. This and several more well-traveled streets were paved. Side roads were dirt and usually so muddy they were called "doroga" which means "bad road" or "you may get there." The main street was full of milling people of all nationalities – Japanese and Chinese with their brightly colored kimonos, Americans, Russians, Tatars, Mongols, Koreans, and others, all speaking a different language.

The Livingstons warned Marie to stay away from the Thieves' Market on the waterfront, because many people had been robbed and killed around that area.

While sightseeing along the outskirts of the city, Marie stumbled upon a makeshift shanty town where thousands of refugees were existing. They had built huts of tin cans, packing crates, scrap lumber, or any available material they could scrounge. Some of the more fortunate had taken over abandoned freight cars for their homes. Many were emaciated and sickly from subsisting on garbage, or black bread, when they could get it. Marie was appalled. The stench reminded her of the barnyard back home.

After a few days exploring the city, Marie decided that she must arrange to return home before her money was entirely gone. Though she had a return ticket, she knew that she must provide for food, and heaven alone knew how long the trip back might take. As she packed, she paused at a knock on her door. Mrs. Livingston stood there holding some of the boxes and the letter she had sent home. Everything but her letter to Nikolai had been returned. Even more shocking was the news that the railroad was no longer running west of Omsk.

Unknown to Marie, freight shipped through Vladivostok from the United States, Britain, and France to aid the White army efforts often ended up in Communist hands, at one time eliciting a letter of thanks from a Red commander. Efforts were made to stop the hijacking. Japan, using any excuse to move in troops, received permission to supply a quota of soldiers; a number they far exceeded, with intentions of having soldiers in place to take over that part of Russia.

Marie was cut off from her family! She was 4,400 miles from

home and there was no way to return! How long would it be before she could see her family again? That night she cried. The Livingstons sympathized and tried to cushion the blow when they told her they were planning to move to Hong Kong. Many businessmen in Vladivostok had already left for Shanghai, America, even Japan, to avoid the Communists, for they felt it was only a matter of time until Vladivostok also fell into Red hands.

Marie had very little money left; she must find work. Determined to overcome the sadness that enveloped her, she embarked on the pursuit of a job. Looking in a newspaper's classified ad section, she found a Help Wanted ad for a girl with good penmanship. Being very naive about big cities and human nature, she eagerly wrote down the address and boarded a street car.

Locating the right number, she stood staring at a two-story structure. She smoothed down her best traveling dress, patted her neatly braided hair coiled on top of her head, and set forth. The office was upstairs. Knees shaking and clutching her purse, she climbed the steps. Nervously she knocked on the door.

"Come in," a brusque voice commanded.

Marie opened the door. An old man with gray hair stood in the outer office.

"I'm here to apply for the job in the paper," Marie stated.

"I want to see an example of your handwriting before I will consider hiring you," the old man said, suggestively running his eyes the full length of her body.

Nervously, Marie wrote several lines on a piece of paper and handed it to the old man.

Upon examining her writing, he looked at her and flashed a yellow-toothed smile. "I would like you to wait."

Marie sat down. There was a knock at the door and another girl entered the small office. The old man had her write several lines also. After looking at her writing, he told her she could leave and he would be in touch with her.

Since Marie really needed the job, she waited and waited. All afternoon she sat until five o'clock. As she got up to leave, the old man came out of the inner office. He walked up to Marie, blocking her path to the door. He reached out and ran his bony fingers down her arm. Surprised, Marie took a step backwards. The old man lifted his other hand and grabbed both her arms, drawing her close to him! His foul breath assailed her nostrils as he tried to kiss her.

Repulsed, Marie grabbed him and slammed him up against the wall. "You want love! I'll give you love!" she shouted as she banged him against the wall again. "Don't you monkey with me!"

Marie's years on the farm had given her strength he hadn't expected; her fluent dialect had deceived him. This was no fragile city girl. Stunned, the old man just stood there and watched as Marie left the office.

There was nothing else listed in the newspaper that night so, desperate for a job, Marie went back to the old man's office. He hadn't fired her. She had good penmanship. She spoke good Russian, not the peasant vernacular. And she could handle the old man's advances. Besides she had put him straight about making any moves on her.

After she worked all day, the old man tried to embrace her again after five o'clock. Prepared this time, Marie dodged his clumsy groping. Once more she slammed him against the wall.

"I am quitting. I told you, 'Don't monkey with me!' I want two days' pay for my time and I will leave and never come back again. This is no good!"

Marie knew she wasn't about to put up with this kind of treatment no matter how badly she needed a job. Collecting her pay, she fled down the steps and raced back to the Livingstons barely able to see through the tears that poured down her cheeks.

Mrs. Livingston met her at the door and, trying to console Marie, asked her what happened. Upon hearing the sordid story Marie gasped out between sobs, Mrs. Livingston said, "In the big city there are lots of traps for girls who are alone. You cannot use the ads; they are just come-ons for innocent girls. You have to have recommendations from someone to get a job."

Marie responded. "I am a country girl and I am not afraid of any kind of work. To heck with this, I am going to get any kind of work I can get."

But even before a job, she must find another place to live. She found an upstairs room, that she hoped she could afford, with a family named Nazarov. Looking out the window in the morning, she saw women carrying lunch buckets. She followed them.

They entered a large warehouse filled with bales of bark. A man was weighing the bundles and then writing the weight in a book. She walked up to him and asked, "Can I get a job here?"

He pointed to a pile of boxes, "Unpack the crates."

Without a moment's hesitation Marie went right to work

unpacking. Soon the man weighing the bales received a telephone call. A line was forming at the scales because no one could read, write, or record the weights. Marie started weighing and marking the weights in the book just as she had seen the man do. The women looked startled. They didn't think Marie knew ABC, because women were not usually educated.

The man returned to the scales. He asked in surprise, "You know how to read and write?"

"Of course, I do!" she exclaimed.

She got the job to weigh and record bales. What a relief! At least now she would be able to pay for a roof over her head and food to eat.

Somewhat suspicious of the newcomer, the girls were none too cordial. But the worst catastrophe arose when she left work one evening to find her velvet cape missing from the peg upon which it always hung. No one professed to knowing a thing about it. Another link with home broken. She could have cried, but held back her tears.

But it was only a few days later that an opportunity arose. The man asked the workers if anyone wanted to help out at the Mayor home. Mr. Mayor owned the plant. Marie responded by raising her hand. She said, "I have been working for other people all my life."

Following directions to reach the Mayor home, she caught the street car to ride across town. She introduced herself to Mrs. Mayora and was put to work washing clothes. Sitting down to lunch and a cup of tea, the two women visited. She asked Marie if she was a Vladivostok girl.

Marie told Mrs. Mayora her story, including her advanced education. Mrs. Mayora had a son and daughter going to college at Tomsk, the only university at that time in all Siberia. Since the Communist takeover just recently, she had not heard from her children. She had no idea what had happened – no mail and no telephone messages. She was extremely worried.

Marie told of her family and how she could not get home because the railroad beyond Omsk was closed. She spoke of the resentment of the other girls because of her ability to read and write and how someone had stolen her velvet cape.

Mrs. Mayora felt that Marie was much too qualified for just housework. She said she would help her find a better job.

When Marie gave her a resume of her work experience, Mrs. Mayora asked, "Would you like to work in a hospital?"

"I am strong. I will do any kind of work. At one time I had hoped to go through nurses' training, but my application arrived too late; classes had already started."

With Mrs. Mayora's recommendation in hand, Marie filled out a form at the hospital the next day. Reading her application, the man behind the desk asked, "Where would you like to work in the hospital?"

"I would like to work with babies, but I will work anywhere."

Supplying her with a white uniform and a white scarf for her head, they sent her to the delivery room to Nurse Ivanova, who proved most unfriendly. She barked orders to Marie, "Put on your apron! Get the patient to bed! Massage the patient's back this way!"

In similar fashion Marie was taught to decide when the doctor must come to examine the patient, to hold the baby's head and gently turn it sideways as it is emerging from the birth canal, to carefully wipe the mouth out and clean the nose, and to hold onto the baby's head to support it.

"Baby will be slicker than snot, so be careful not to let it slip out of your hands. Don't let it come too fast. Tie the cord. Cut it. Let the afterbirth come naturally. Take the baby. Bathe it. Put a name tag on it and put it in the crib."

Screams from the women in labor echoing throughout the hospital wing sent chills up Marie's spine. She was not accustomed to such racket. The first day she helped deliver five babies. She had never done anything like this, but she would learn! The sight of all the blood, amniotic fluid and after-births nauseated her and it took her some time to adjust. She kept repeating the orders in her mind that the head nurse had given her.

By the end of the day, and five babies later, she knew the procedure by heart. As she held the newborn babies in her arms, all covered with blood and fluid, and as she heard them cry for the first time, she knew she was participating in one of God's miracles.

The first week was difficult, trying to get used to the crying and moaning – some women made a lot of noise. But the second week was better. By now she was able to tune out the noise and take Nurse Ivanova's abrasive commands. She became so efficient that within two months another doctor wanted her to work in his dentist's office. Nurse Ivanova refused to let her go. She complimented Marie's work and Marie was proud to stay.

She continued to remain with the Mayors for the first weeks. One day she arrived there to find a Chinese tailor with a measuring tape. Upon orders of Mrs. Mayora he was to make her a wool coat. Overwhelmed, she stood silently as he quickly did his job and left.

"I have no money yet, but I will repay you."

"No, this is a gift from me to you. Please accept it."

Marie was only able to nod her head. No one but family had been so kind before.

Her hours soon made it necessary to move into the quarters supplied for the nurses and aids. She shared the sparsely furnished room with seven others. Each woman had a bed and a table. Under the table were drawers for any personal items. There was plenty of room for Marie's meager possessions. Her new coat was carefully folded into a drawer she could lock.

Meals were provided by the hospital, so she did not have to worry about standing in bread lines for hours to buy her food, which was a daily chore for most women in Vladivostok.

During her first month at the hospital, Mrs. Livingston had come by the hospital to tell Marie goodbye. They were on their way to Hong Kong. She brought a letter with her that had arrived for Marie. Marie was sad at the parting, but with one glance at the letter she saw it was from Irkutsk and had to be from Nikolai. He must have written it almost right away; she had given him the Livingston's address. Had he received her letter? There was no time to read the letter at work. She would read it when she returned to the dormitory.

With a song in her heart and a smile on her face, Marie carried out her duties for the rest of the day. When she had a moment of spare time, she would lovingly take the letter from her pocket and just look at it, picturing Nikolai, as she stared at the envelope.

The day dragged. Finally, her shift was over and sitting down on her bed near the window, Marie carefully removed the letter from her pocket. Strong bold lettering on the front of the envelope reminded her of how straight and tall Nikolai stood, with such an air of confidence, even though, she knew, his injury sometimes still hurt.

Eagerly she broke the seal and slid out the neatly penned letter. Enclosed with the letter was a small picture of him and a beautiful poem that Nikolai had written just for her. Conflicting emotions arose as Marie read the letter and poem. How could one be so happy and so sad at the same time? Nikolai was sweet and he wished that he had been able to spend more time with her, so he could get to know her better. He was being sent back to Omsk and then to Tyumen, where there was now bitter fighting between the Reds and the Whites. Marie's heart sank when she read that he would be back in the thick of the fighting. Thrilled to hear from him, but sad about the facts the letter contained, she tried to sort through her feelings.

She hadn't known it was possible to feel so alone. Cut off from her family, knowing no one but the people at the hospital, separated from friends and relatives, she could not stop the tears. Ashamed at her weakness, she glanced around to see whether anyone had noticed. Hurriedly wiping her eyes, she again read Nikolai's wonderful poem and smiled at the message.

Work was the answer. She would not let herself be overcome with emotion, feeling sorry for herself. Work was something that would comfort her. She had worked all her life and now it would keep a roof over her head and food in her stomach. Actually, she was much more fortunate than those poor people living in the makeshift camps surrounding the city.

Marie still shuddered as she recalled her walk the day she discovered those poor people. She remembered the dirty, hungry children staring at her with their big, solemn, pleading eyes; the stench of human waste permeating the air; the squalid shacks thrown together, and the human forms huddled inside. Such a contrast to the fields of flowers and blooming roses just a mile further from town.

There were miles and miles of beautiful meadows adorned with wild flowers – fresh, clean, fragrant. These refugees, too, had once stood tall, proud, smelling of soap and fresh air until their bodies and very souls had been trampled upon by the greed for power that spends lives so freely. They were a patch of human beings stomped into the ground by those with political aspirations and the changing winds of times that pitted human beings against each other. Cast out of their homes like wilted flowers, they were searching for a place they could call home where once again they could bloom and flourish. Had it not been for the Livingstons and the Mayors she might easily have been one of the refugees in that camp. She was deeply grateful for the kindnesses they had shown her. Indeed, she had been fortunate and she would not be a whiner!

The opportunity to learn nursing skills might make a difference in her life; she was going to learn all she could. She would work hard. She would save her money so that she could go home someday.

The hospital was over-crowded and under-staffed. Sometimes one hospital ward of two hundred patients would have only one nurse on duty. Marie was glad she was in the obstetrical ward because the rest of the hospital would have as many as two thousand patients with typhus, cholera, or typhoid fever. At least these people received some care. In the freight yards, there were thousands at a time infected with disease, and no doctors or nurses available to tend them. Death stalked the halls of the hospital and streets of the city.

Mrs. Mayora visited Marie at the hospital and told her they were moving to Shanghai because the Communists were advancing along the Trans-Siberian Railroad and seizing control of everything. After October 14, 1919, there had been no trains out of Petrograd.

Marie's thoughts flew immediately to Nikolai. Had he been killed? Had he been taken prisoner? Was it true the Reds didn't bother to take prisoners? How she wished she could learn whether he was safe. What about her family? Surely the Communists wouldn't bother with a town so small as Antipina. Would they?

Mrs. Mayora had continued to talk and Marie concentrated once more on what she was saying – something about making arrangements for Marie to go with them. Thanking Mrs. Mayora for all her help and concern, Marie declined the offer.

"If you ever change your mind, we will help you get to Shanghai should you be ready to join us."

Marie had been at the hospital for several months when a twelve-year-old boy, Ramon Kochetkov, showed up looking for work or any kind of odd jobs. He carried a balalaika, a triangular shaped guitar. Marie asked him if he could play it. He enthusiastically demonstrated that, indeed, he played extremely well. Marie hummed, then sang along. The hospital staff liked the industrious youngster, kept him working at various jobs, and secretly sneaked him food.

One day Marie asked, "Ramon, do you live here in the city?"

"No, Ma'am," he replied with bowed head. "I am an orphan," he mumbled in a faint voice so low Marie could hardly hear him. "I live in the streets."

Sitting down beside Ramon, Marie quietly listened as he told his sad story. "My parents and I had to leave home because the Communists were moving in. Once my father was able to buy tickets on the railroad, and we were aboard, we thought everyone would be safe. But the train was so dirty and there were rats and lice and fleas. The mosquitoes were bad enough, but the lice were worse. We were all scratching and itching. It was awful."

Ramon paused, choking up as he remembered, "My mother came down with a fever, headache, and then broke out in red spots all over her body. She died." His eyes streamed. When he could speak, he continued," They wouldn't give us time to bury her. We had to leave her body alongside the railroad ties."

Ramon looked up at Marie with pain and sorrow etched on his innocent, young face. "Papa was so distraught; he would not talk. Then he became ill. Before he died, he made me promise to go to Petropalovsk. That is on the Kamchatka Peninsula," he injected for her benefit. "My brother lives there. He is a teacher. We were all going to join him. When Papa died some other passengers just threw his body off the train, and I couldn't stop them." He sobbed quietly.

Marie gave a groan of sympathy and revulsion at the horror the boy must have felt.

Ramon, now composed, explained, "They were afraid they would die too if they didn't get rid of the body."

How could one so young be so understanding of such barbaric acts? Marie put her arm around Ramon's slender shoulders and gave him a hug. She knew how much loss she felt, knowing she couldn't return home. Ramon's pain was much greater because he had watched both parents die and now he was an orphan. At least she could hope that someday, when the fighting was over, she could return home; Ramon's separation was final.

Typhus and cholera ran rampant on the railroad and in the improvised refugee camps. Now both Ramon's parents' bodies were forsaken, lying along the rails, denied a decent burial. So prevalent were the deaths along the railroad, that even a blanket in which to wrap bodies could no longer be spared. Upon arriving in Vladivostok, Ramon had been living by his wits alone.

After hearing Ramon's story, the administrator at the hospital hired him as a handyman with quarters in the hospital complex. In the evenings Ramon would show up at the dormitory with his balalaika and play music for the nurses. Marie joined him, singing different Russian songs. The nurses would shout, "Bravo! Bravo!" and ask for more. That was one of the few happy times.

Vladivostok was a political cauldron. Millions of tons of supplies had piled up with no transportation to move them. Fleeing refugees packed the streets and hillsides. White Russian soldiers tried to maintain peace in the city, but the Japanese troops that had been allowed into the city to "help protect the Japanese business interests" and the Japanese who were living there, became assertive. Shots could be heard day and night. The town was no longer safe from the Japanese armed troops.

In the obstetric ward, Marie was assisting with a delivery when bullets smashed through the windows of the room. Screams pierced the air. Nurses' shouts mingled with the frightened shrieks of the women in labor. Flying glass peppered the room. Bullets hitting the wall sent plaster showering down to the floor. Everyone dove for cover under the beds and delivery tables. Suddenly the hospital, though it was in the middle of the city, was under siege by the Japanese. For a week no one ventured outside the hospital complex.

As soon as the White army halted the siege, Mrs. Nazarova sought out Marie at the hospital. The Nazarovs had two children, a boy of eight and a girl, six. The short time Marie had stayed with them, she had spent time in the evenings giving them lessons in reading and writing. They were very polite children and eager to learn. She had kept in touch with them after she moved into the dormitory. The Nazarovs had decided it was too dangerous to remain in Vladivostok. Rumors about the vast amount of gold available in Kamchatka offered a more acceptable alternative. In order to get away from the turmoil, and to get rich mining gold, they were going north to seek their fortune.

They invited Marie to come along. They wanted her to tutor the children and offered her the position of bookkeeper. She would be a shareholder in the company. They planned to stay for just a year; by then they would all be rich, the fighting would be over, and it would be safe to return. They had purchased plenty of supplies to last a year and they assured her there was plenty for her too.

Aware of the deteriorating conditions in Vladivostok, Marie thought their offer sounded good. Since they assured her they would be gone only a year and she could get enough money to go home, she decided to go with them.

When she told Ramon about her decision to go to Kamchatka, he begged her to take him along. Petropalovsk, where his brother lived, was right on the way.

"I have no money for a ticket for you. I had to borrow money for my own ticket." Marie explained to Ramon. Marie hated telling Ramon she was leaving, for they had grown close and Marie felt protective of him. "Besides you have no passport."

A passport was needed to make the trip because the boat stopped in Japan for several days to pick up cargo. Marie's passport had expired, so she asked Nurse Tamara to sign for an extension for one year.

Now, how to resolve the problem of getting Ramon on the ship. "Boy, come with me. I will see what I can do."

She took Ramon to the dock where the TOMSK was moored, loading supplies. She sought out the cook and told him Ramon's story. The cook said that if Ramon was willing to peel potatoes and wash dishes, he would help get him to Petropalovsk, free.

Elated, Ramon and Marie hurried back to pack. Ramon still had a problem. It was impossible to get him a passport since he did not have a living guardian. Marie told Ramon the only way he could get by without a passport was to remain on the TOMSK all the time they were at Otoru, Hokkaido, when they stopped to take on cargo. If he were to go on shore, he would have to stay there forever. He would not be allowed to return with no passport. Ramon agreed.

All was in readiness for another adventure.

CHAPTER ELEVEN

AT NATURE'S MERCY ON THE TOMSK

On June 21, 1920, the TOMSK pulled away from the dock in Vladivostok into the Sea of Japan. On board was a happy Ramon, the Nazarov family, Marie, and many other passengers, as well as cargo headed for the northeastern Siberian coast and Kamchatka Peninsula. What did it matter that they all had to share the cramped quarters? By all accounts, they were headed for fields of gold so rich, one merely had to pick the nuggets off the beach.

The weather was clear and there was a slight breeze blowing. Watching the skyline of Vladivostok shrink smaller and smaller as the TOMSK sailed farther and farther out to sea, Marie was having second thoughts. The turmoil and fighting was left behind, and for that, she was glad. But she frowned as she thought about her family; she was traveling further away from home instead of closer.

Horror stories about the advancing Red Army's atrocities concerned Marie. Thousands of Russians had lost their lives since the Bolshevik Revolution started. She hoped and prayed that Nikolai was not one of the casualties. Pulling the well-read poem from her bag, she again pored over Nikolai's words that had been written just for her, though by now she had it memorized and again she looked at the picture for reassurance.

With heavy heart she watched the coastline disappear on the horizon.

The gently swaying deck distracted her from her lonely thoughts as the mild slapping of the waves against the boat's hull whispered the song of the sea. At least she was able to help Ramon on his journey to be reunited with part of his family.

Churning its way north, the coal-burning TOMSK, belching black sooty smoke from the barrel-shaped smokestacks, slowly steamed through the Sea of Japan. The huge hungry furnace consumed tons of coal as the throbbing engine turned the giant propellers.

The gentle roll of the ship was soothing to Marie as she leaned against the rail watching the horizon where the coastline had now totally disappeared. In any direction, all she could see was water. Looking at Ramon, she noticed his stricken white face. He stood gripping the rail so tightly his knuckles were white.

"Are you all right, Ramon?" she asked, putting an arm around his shoulders.

"I'll be all right as soon as the ship stops rolling, Ma'am." he squeaked between clenched teeth. "I am not used to the sea."

A haunted expression flitted across his thin, pale face. "I can't help but think about Mama and Papa. They were supposed to be with me on this journey." Gulping down the lump in his throat, he continued," My father told me to be strong, and I am trying – but, oh, if only my mother could tousle my hair again and Papa pat me on the back and tell me everything will be just fine." With a semblance of a smile, he confided, "Really, I hated having my hair messed, but I wouldn't mind a bit now." He blinked back tears.

"Nothing has been the same since the Communists sent us running for our lives like a pack of dogs after a deer. I don't understand why my parents were being hunted for supporting the White army. I am trying to be brave, but things are pretty confusing. I am so glad you could bring me along. You are my only friend."

"Come, I'll take you down to the room."

A large room on the lower deck was shared by Marie, Ramon, the Nazarovs and other passengers, among them the old man, Nicholai Clernesko, in his sixties, who had begged the Nazarovs to take him with them.

Ramon let go of the railing and grabbed Marie's arm in a death grip as she led him down the stairs.

"Maybe, if you lie down awhile, you will get used to the ship's motion," she murmured softly as she tucked a blanket around him.

"He looks so vulnerable," thought Marie, staring down at his boyish, innocent face. "Too young to be on his own – another victim of circumstances beyond his control."

Awaking, Ramon stretched. He felt much better; his stomach seemed to have adjusted to the swaying. He reported to the kitchen to carry out his duties as cook's helper.

Marie filled much of her time crocheting. In the evening when his work was through, Ramon would play his balilaika while she would sing.

Time passed quickly.

"Land ahoy, starboard!" brought everyone rushing to the main deck to see the jagged outline of land on the right hand side of the cargo ship.

Marie and Ramon made their way forward to the bow where they could watch as the TOMSK approached Otaru, Japan. Riding the wave crests, seagulls bobbed on the blue-green water. The rocky coastline was a haven for sea gulls and other birds. Coming closer to port, they could see the many square-sailed Japanese and Chinese junks. Marie had seen many of these Chinese and Japanese boats in the harbor at Vladivostok so she easily recognized their unique shapes. The large sail was made of puckered vertical strips of cloth or canvas stitched side by side. Hanging limply on the masts, the sails resembled giant gathered shirts until the wind filled them.

Passing many junks manned by two people, Marie could see the fishing nets and baskets used by the divers to pluck oysters with their precious pearls from the bottom of the ocean. Ishikari Bay, located on the northeast side of Hokkaido Island was a stopover port for most trading vessels. The captain had informed them that they would be spending three days at Otaru to trade goods and restock their supply of coal.

"I wish I could go ashore with you," lamented Ramon, as they watched the TOMSK's crew drop the big anchor, causing a great splash and spraying them with salt water.

"Now you knew when we set out, that you could not leave the ship," reproved Marie, though she inwardly sympathized with him. "You must remain below deck. If you leave the ship, you will not be allowed to get back on board because you do not have a passport."

The throbbing engines gave a final burping sigh. A brief startling silence was broken by the crew's bustling about, mooring the ship to the dock.

Marie went below to get her bag. She joined the Nazarovs at the bulwarks watching and waiting for the gang plank to be lowered. The crew was already opening the hatches and lifting with rope nets the cargo that was to be delivered ashore.

Stepping out on the solid dock, Marie had the eerie feeling the ground was moving. But it was not long before her sea-legs gave way to land-legs and it felt good to be off the constantly moving deck of the ship.

Marie and the Nazarovs walked into Otaru, a small trading port and the sea entry for a town not far away – Sapporo, the capital of Hokkaido, the second largest island of Japan. Hokkaido did not become important to Japan until after the war with Russia. Fear of a territorial grab sparked colonization. Mostly mountains and forest, only about ten per cent of the land was under cultivation. Poor soil and cooler climate lent itself more to grazing and pasture, and dairying became the foremost industry, though oats. wheat, rye, white potatoes, sugar, and the most important crop, rice, were cultivated. The sea here provided about twenty percent of Japan's fish tonnage.

Making their way to the market district, Marie turned to Mrs. Nazarov and in a low voice, said, "I am surprised. Some of the Japanese selling the merchandise in the booths have blue eyes, wavy black hair, and are tall. In Vladiovostok, they were short, with brown eyes, and very straight black hair."

Mrs. Nazarov explained, "They are Ainus, of Caucasoid descent, whereas the Japanese are Mongoloid. The Ainus are the original natives of Hokkaido."

She continued, "I wish I could afford one of these beautiful silk kimonos." She said wistfully, "All our money went to purchase supplies for our expedition. Maybe we will find so much gold, I can buy a dozen of these."

Brilliantly colored fabrics hanging in front of the booth flapped lazily in the wind in the open market. Beautiful fine silk kimonos were displayed for sale and Marie agreed, "It would be nice." How she wished she had the money to buy one.

Ornately carved ivory knickknacks lined shelves and wall-hangings of birds, flowers, and mountains were suspended from pieces of bamboo.

Watching the Japanese eat with chopsticks was a novelty to Marie. She was perplexed. How anyone could actually pick up food with two sticks? Excited about seeing all the strange new sights in this different country, Marie could visualize Barbara's reaction to all the exotic fabrics and costumes that she was seeing for the first time.

"I can make flowers like this," Marie stated as she gingerly lifted one of the delicate paper flowers displayed in ornately painted China vases. Religious carvings and small tea cups and teapots were painted with picturesque scenes of birds and flowers. This was a totally new world to Marie!

By the third day, they were ready to continue their journey north. On board, Marie watched the crews bringing newly traded cargo into the holds.

The captain told her, "We will be ready to sail just as soon as they finish stowing these last containers of tea. We have to be sure the weight of the load is evenly spread across the beam of the ship so we will ride even in the water. With too much weight on one side, we will lean that way and the ship will be harder to steer."

Just then the ship's bell chimed four times indicating the time was 2:00 P.M. The first mate had explained to Marie that the day on the ship consisted of six four-hour watches. The bell rang every half hour to mark how many half-hours had elapsed since the watch changed. Watches changed every four hours. The end of the first half-hour, the bell rang once; the end of the second half-hour, twice, and so on, until it rang eight times to signal the end of each watch. Then the bell cycle would start all over again.

Going below, Marie tried to find Ramon to tell him about the incredible sights she had seen and the very different music she had heard while walking through the market place. A deep rumbling from the bowels of the ship told her that they would soon be casting off. A surge of excitement washed over her. They were headed for the gold fields! Soon she would be picking up nuggets off the beach on Kamchatka Peninsula. She would not only earn enough money to go home, she would also go home with extra money! She would buy Barbara gaily decorated silk fabrics for her sewing shop. Wouldn't Papa be proud! He had taught her to always make the best deal.

"And, under the circumstances," she thought, "I did make the best choice to go north to look for gold. It will be a lot of work, but I'm not afraid of work – I've done it all my life. Surely the gold fields can't be as chaotic as Vladivostok. I wonder if the Communists have seized control yet." Soberly she gazed out a porthole, watching the mooring lines being cast away.

Adrift, severed from the security of the dock, the big engines drove the propellers and the rudder guided the TOMSK as it slipped out toward open ocean. Marie felt as though she was being propelled into uncharted waters. Guided by a desire to survive, she put her faith in God and hoped that she had made the right decisions. She wondered if the Gypsies had ever felt doubts like this as they traveled on their journeys throughout Siberia.

Lightning flashed and thunder cracked, startling Marie awake. Pitching and groaning, the TOMSK was being battered by high winds and heavy seas. It took Marie a moment to realize where she was and what was happening.

A scream pierced the air as Mrs. Nazarov woke up. "We're going to die!" she sobbed as she clutched her husband and drew her children to her.

No one was sleeping now. Ramon scooted over to Marie and grabbed her arm. He was trembling. She put her arm around him to comfort him. Skittering and rolling, loose items slid around the floor as the TOMSK collided with another wave. Wildly swinging lamps banged on the heavy beams overhead.

Usually calm prevailed this time of year, but a storm had come up very suddenly. The weather had been so nice up until now. Shuddering the boat plunged head-on into the towering wall of water, blocking any light from the porthole. Marie began to pray.

The ship felt like a giant hand was pushing it backward instead of going forward. The wind whistled overhead through the rigging. Flailing, the TOMSK's huge propellor spun uselessly in the air as the ship balanced on the crest of a giant wave. The huge twirling blades howled in protest until once again they sliced into the foaming water, only to be exposed once more with the next wave, jolting the ship as it plunged into wave after wave.

"How can the ship continue to take such a battering?" thought Marie as she braced herself for another bone-jarring jolt. One arm was still around Ramon whose body never stopped shaking. His terrified, vise-like grip was hurting her arm.

Light began to filter in through the porthole when it wasn't covered with water. "Dawn is breaking, Ramon." she reassured him. "Now the weather should get better."

"I hope so," he quavered.

But the storm raged on through the day. Ramon was too sick to go to work in the galley, but then no one felt much like eating anyway. The sickening odor of vomit permeated the stuffy cabin air.

Marie felt as though she had been riding a bucking horse for hours; the only difference was that she could get off a horse onto solid ground, but down here there was no easy way to get off the ship. She tried to stand and walk, but the erratic gyrations of the cabin floor made it impossible to keep her balance.

Water seeped in around the porthole. When the ship was headed straight into the waves, the action was up and down. When the ship was blown broadside to the waves, it wallowed back and forth like a barrel, with water washing over the sides. She felt like the whole world was in constant motion, and her stomach reeled. Closing her eyes, she willed herself not to give in to her queasy stomach.

As evening fell, the waves became smaller and the ship stopped bucking and the lunging calmed. Marie stood. Cramped muscles screamed at her as she flexed her arms. She realized how tightly she had gripped Ramon, who had fallen asleep, totally exhausted, sprawled on his blanket on the floor.

Climbing to the main deck Marie met haggard, exhausted seamen hurrying with hand tools. Listening to the excited chatter between the sailors, she overheard, "hole in the ship" and "taking on water."

"What did you say?" Marie blurted as she grabbbed one seaman by the sleeve.

"During the storm, a log knocked a hole in the bow of the boat."

"Are we sinking?" an icy fear in her voice.

"No, Ma'am," the older sailor replied. "Don't you worry. We patched the hold and the pumps are sucking out the water we took on. Storm blew us a little off course, but now everything is under control."

The idea of traveling had always appealed to Marie but she hadn't dreamed it could be so scary. Surviving the storm was what her life had come to be, day by day. This past year, she had been tossed to and fro by the tempest that was drowning her country – the death of the Czar and the fighting that had embroiled the entire nation, terrorizing all peoples. Was there no safe place anymore? How secure Papa's house had seemed.

As they often did, her thoughts shifted to Nikolai. She prayed he was still alive.

Returning to the cabin, she said nothing about what she had learned. There was no need to alarm the others now. The danger was over. Though the storm and heavy seas had subsided, the wind was still blowing. Everyone was exhausted.

Loneliness crept in as she sat down on her pallet. A tear trickled down her cheek as she realized that if the TOMSK had sunk, her family would never have known what happened to her. Too weary to think any longer, she fell asleep.

After the storm the TOMSK continued to make the scheduled stops at settlements in the Kuril Islands, dropping off supplies and cargo and picking up food and fuel. Marie enjoyed seeing the small towns.

Ramon was becoming very anxious to reach Petropalovak, on the tip of the Kamchatka Peninsula, where his brother lived.

Finally, on a slightly cloudy day, the TOMSK, deftly steered around the rocky shoals at the entrance, glided into the mirror-still waters of Petropalovsk Bay. Snugly sheltered by a horsehoe arrangement of surrounding hills, the calm, clear bay offered welcome relief from the ocean waves. The low hills were dotted with houses encircling the bay.

Square-sailed Chinese and Japanese junks, as well as trading ships from Germany, Holland, England, and the United States, sat motionless, their reflections mirrored in the glass smooth water. The bay's bottom of soft cushioning sand allowed boats to pull close to shore, for when the shallow tide receded, boats simply nestled in the sand until the tide once more washed around them, gently refloating them.

Throbbing sounds from the TOMSK's coal-fired engines echoed off the hills. Then all was quiet.

Impatiently jumping up and down beside Marie at the railing, Ramon blurted, "What if I can't find my brother? He doesn't even know I'm coming."

"We will find him."

"It will be hard for me to tell him about Mama and Papa," he worried as he bowed his head. "Do you think he will recognize me?"

After the TOMSK was securely moored and the gangplank lowered, Marie and Ramon embarked on their search for his brother. The town was celebrating a holiday and many people were in the street. Marie asked an elderly man if he knew where the Kochetkovs lived. With only one thousand population, it was not surprising that he recognized the name as that of a local teacher. He pointed out the street and gave them directions.

Ramon raced down the street.

"Ramon, wait for me!" Marie gasped as she hurried to keep up with the excited boy.

"Hurry," he shouted impatiently over his shoulder as he raced up the hill.

Marie could not keep up but certainly did not blame him for being in a hurry to be reunited with his brother.

Breathing hard, they arrived at the rectangular two-storied house the old man had described. Ramon was standing still, staring at the house. "What if they don't want me?"

"Go knock on the door and introduce yourself."

Hesitantly Ramon lifted his hand and gently knocked. Opening the door was a short, stocky woman wearing a scarf on her head and an apron.

"Are you Mrs. Kochetkov?"

"Yes, I am."

"Then you must be my brother's wife!"

Just then a man came to see what was going on. Ramon would recognize him anywhere because he looked just like his papa.

"I am Ramon."

With a gasp of amazement, "Ramon!" the big man opened wide his arms.

Ramon flew into the welcoming arms, and through his tears, he blurted, "Mama and Papa are both dead. We ran from the Communists, but they got sick on the train and died and I couldn't help them."

Clasped in loving arms, he sobbed out his grief to his brother who was now crying quietly as well.

After some highly emotional moments, Ramon's brother noticed Marie standing in the door. His wife was too stunned to remember she should be welcoming the guest. As Ramon introduced her he explained that but for Marie he would never have made it.

The brother tried to express his deep gratitude to Marie for taking care of Ramon. He invited her to stay overnight with them.

The next day, they took her sight-seeing around the town. Marie enjoyed walking on solid ground for a change. They visited a monument that commemorated a short battle in which they had defeated England years before.

Marie learned that Petropalovsk was named by combining the names of Vitus Bering's two ships, PETER and PAUL, used on his voyages of discovery in the Pacific. She also was told that about one-third of the people in the town were oriental. The Japanese were financiers; the Chinese, shopkeepers; and the Koreans predominantly laborers. They all had gardens though growing vegetables was not easy because of the frequent rains and clouds. Root crops, such as potatoes, carrots, beets, and turnips did well.

They stopped to watch the fishermen with their nets made of nettles. Here nettles grew eight or nine feet tall and were harvested in the fall. Carding the stems, like flax to make linen, they produced a tough fiber to make the nets that only lasted for a season because of the salt water. Interested in the weaving Marie was warned not to get too close for a nettle sting was most unpleasant.

The Kochetkovs urged Marie to stay in Petropalovsk and promised to find her a job. They said many who had gone further north on the Kamchatka Peninsula to find gold had never returned. Food was scarce and many had died of hunger, scurvy, or had frozen to death.

Marie returned to the boat and told the Nazarovs what she had learned.

"We have plenty of food to last a long time and we have onions to prevent scurvy. We are prepared. There is much gold to be found and the old man is going to teach us how to find the gold. Please stay with us," the Nazarovs persuaded.

"I do want to make money so I can travel home and go back to school. I guess I will stay with you since it will only be for a year," Marie decided.

It was difficult for her to say good-bye to Ramon for she had grown fond of him and he seemed like a little brother. The evening before she left, Ramon played his balalaika while she sang. Marie was glad that Ramon now had part of his family to love and care for him.

Little did she realize the tough life she had selected for herself or the perilous journey she was undertaking. She had weathered the fierce storm so far. After all, things couldn't get much worse. Or could they?

CHAPTER TWELVE

ARRIVAL AT INDIAN POINT

During the one and one-half months the TOMSK wound a slow pace north, they continued stopping at posts and towns along the way to drop off supplies and pick up furs. The decks of the boat were loaded with barrels, stacks of lumber, and other building materials needed by the isolated villages. Flour, sugar, grain, tobacco, tea, and other food supplies were stored below deck out of the weather.

"I must go into Anadyr and obtain a permit for us to stay at the Indian Point schoolhouse," Mr. Nazarov said to Marie as they stood watching the approaching shoreline dotted with houses. "Mr. Cherneskow tells me the school has been abandoned because the war has cut off communication and supplies. Mr. Pavlov, the teacher, was not getting paid so he moved to Provideniya. I'm sure that the school would be a good place to live."

Marie knew nothing of Provideniya so responded with a question, "Who do you have to get permission from?"

"The Russian Administration Office," he answered, staring across the small bay as the TOMSK slowly approached the dock. "I've been told that Anadyr was started by the Cossacks in 1649. Last December the Anadyr Underground Revolutionary Communists seized control and arrested Kolchak's Whites who were in power. The Communists revoked all fishing and trading rights of foreign countries and their local merchants. Kolchak and his followers, who were mostly Chukchi natives, turned the tables and executed all the Communists they found. Rumor has it the Communists are trying to regain control. I really don't know whom we will have to negotiate with," he added worriedly.

"You mean after we came all this way to get away from the Communists, that they may be in control here?"

"We'll just have to wait and see. I suggest you stay on board with the rest of our party while I go ashore to check things out."

Marie was more than happy to avoid any possible contact with Communists. Her goal was to get enough money to go home, and she wanted no part of the revolution.

Because the Czar had ignored the Siberian coast so long as the furs continued to pour into Western Russia, the natives were accustomed to self-governing. Traders were somewhat affected by governmental regulation because they supposedly were to obtain permits to carry on trade with the natives. The Whites were involved in the war and did not interfere. They did not have the boats or manpower to check who had permits and who did not. Also smoke from the slow coal-burning Russian boats was easily discernable against the horizon and thus they were easy for foreign ships to evade.

The Communist policy toward the natives angered the Chukchis because the Reds forced them to take whatever they brought to trade even though the items were not needed or wanted. Furs were devalued, causing a drastic drop in the standard of living. Needless to say, the natives were most unhappy under the Communists and helped the Whites whenever possible.

Mr. Nazarov returned to the TOMSK, his face beaming. "We have a permit to live in the schoolhouse this winter. We won't have to build a shelter."

Dropping anchor in Indian Bay several days after leaving Anadyr, the TOMSK bobbed gently on the waves just offshore from the Indian Bay schoolhouse. Staring at the bleak, desolate land surrounding the schoolhouse, Marie was disheartened. There were no trees, and nothing moved. The weather-beaten clapboard building provided the only break in the stark horizon. She felt as alone as that schoolhouse, abandoned on the barren tundra.

Unloading their food, blankets, mining equipment, and trade goods into a small boat, the crew lightered them ashore. How good it felt to stand on solid ground after almost two months at sea, knowing she was not going to have to get back aboard the boat. The Nazarov children ran up and down the beach, happy to be free to run and play. The cramped ship's cabin had not allowed for any such activity.

Walking toward the schoolhouse, wooden satchel in hand, Marie had the sensation that the ground rose to meet her with each step. She felt the wobbling diminish as her land-legs returned. Marie was ready to grab a shovel and start digging. After two months of enforced idleness, with activity limited to crocheting, physical labor would feel good. She had never been accustomed to sitting around.

The door creaked on rusty hinges as Marie entered the dark schoolhouse. Looking around her, she realized she was standing in a classroom. Adjoining was a kitchen with a huge brick stove with a built-in iron plate on top. Not just for cooking, the stove was designed to provide heat for the entire building. Exploring the rest of the building, she discovered there were several rooms. Good! Each person could have his own space.

Excitement built up as Marie thought about the gold she would find on the beach. Hurriedly disposing of her satchel, she dashed back to the beach to help carry the goods and supplies. The sooner the moving-in was finished, the sooner she could start digging and panning for gold!

Unloading was quickly accomplished and supplies stowed away when Mr. Cherneskow asked, "Marie will you help me with the firewood?"

Taking her response for granted, he turned to go out the door.

Drat! Well the gold would wait. How could she refuse him? He was in his sixties. He and Mr. Nazarov had been partners in a store in Vladivostok. He wanted nothing to do with the Communists so any alternative looked good to him. Marie noted the expensive clothes on his slight frame and realized that he had been accustomed to refinements that certainly did not exist in this forbidding land.

By now the TOMSK was just a speck in the distance, its telltale stream of black sooty smoke belching forth from its huge smokestack. Now they were all alone. Turning her eyes back to the desolate landscape, Marie stood shivering. She pulled her wool coat tighter around her and headed for the woodpile.

A large pile of driftwood had been gathered from the shore and dragged close to the school. Mr. Cherneskow grabbed one end of a cross-cut saw and Marie took the other.

"I hope you can keep up with me," Mr. Cherneskow chuckled as he positioned the saw on the log. "You pull toward you, and I will pull it back toward me. Don't push the saw or the blade will bend."

"You are in for a surprise, old man," thought Marie as she pulled the saw toward her. The sharp jagged teeth of the saw slashed into the dry wood, making a grating sound as sawdust fell to the ground.

After fifteen or twenty minutes, Mr. Cherneskow was sweating and gasping for breath. "We should have enough for a day or two," he panted while wiping the perspiration from his forehead with his sleeve.

"I'll carry this into the house and start a fire." Marie suppressed a smile. She wasn't even winded. Her many years of working in the fields had conditioned her body. Two months of inactivity may cause her muscles to be a little sore in the morning, but Mr. Cherneskow probably would have difficulty getting out of bed.

Floating ice at sea warned them that winter was fast approaching. The ducks and geese flying south signaled snow would soon be falling.

Mr. Cherneskow persevered in spite of the aches and pains he refused to acknowledge, and he and Marie cut an ample supply of firewood. Often while she gave the children their lessons, he would use an axe showing more determination than skill.

The men patrolled the beach constantly searching and hoping to find sufficient wood to last the long winter.

Meeting an Eskimo hunting party, they invited them back to the school to offer them some tobacco to trade for fresh meat. From that point on, the Eskimoes, who lived nearby, brought different kinds of meat and hides – deer, wolverine, seal, and fish – whatever they were fortunate enough to catch, to trade for much-desired tobacco. Smoking had been introduced to the Eskimoes many years before. When tobacco was unavailable, they smoked seaweed in hand carved pipes. Chewing tobacco was shared. One chew might be passed around from mouth to mouth until all had enjoyed a chew. It was a poor host who did not share his tobacco chew.

The days became progressively shorter as the weather became colder. The sea was covered with ice. Walking along the shore one day, the two men were caught in a blizzard. When they started out, the weather was calm. By afternoon, a blinding snow storm swooped in and obliterated all landmarks; blowing snow and ice crystals stung like sharp sand. Becoming disoriented, they wandered erratically until darkness fell. They accidently stumbled out onto the thin ice. Crashing through the ice, they soaked their feet and legs in the cold, salty seawater. Frantically, they thrashed and kicked as they broke ice out of the way. Fur-lined mittens were drenched as they worked their way to shore, shoving the ice aside with their hands. At last, recognizing the shoreline, they struggled back to the schoolhouse with frozen, numb limbs. Too exhausted and too stiff from cold to remove their frozen wet garments, the men were forced to allow Marie and Mrs. Nazarova to undress them. The women quickly stripped them and tried to warm them by submerging their hands and feet in lukewarm water. Many weeks passed before either man could use his hands or walk on his frost-bitten feet.

Bitter cold gripped the barren tundra showing no mercy to the unwary. Survival against the elements was no game. One mistake meant instant death. Those who challenged the elements and survived developed a deep respect for the unforgiving, ferocious whims of the weather, the animals, and the ocean. Those who mocked and ignored nature's warnings just disappeared without a trace.

"I'm worried about Mr. Cherneskow," Anna Nazarov said in a low voice to Marie. "He refuses to eat any wild game and has had no meat since we arrived. Ever since he fell through the ice, he has been sick. I don't know what to do for him. He is losing his teeth and I fear he has scurvy."

"We can't force him to eat meat. He won't even taste the broth I made from the boiled walrus flipper. I grind it fine and add onions and spices. I think it's very good but he just turns up his nose at it," Marie spoke softly.

"I know. But you think he would try in order to stay alive."

"It's his choice. We have plenty of ducks, geese, fish, and deer meat. He won't even try them," sighed Marie.

Howling winds blew down from the Arctic, pelting the schoolhouse at Indian Bay with its drifting snow. Nights were so long with barely a scant period of daylight. Locked in the jaws of a Siberian winter, Marie felt as much a prisoner as one behind bars. Never had she felt so isolated. She could now understand why political prisoners had been banished to Siberia to serve their sentences. There may be no bars, but nature's fury held them in its grip as securely as concrete and steel ever could.

Marie crocheted and helped the children with their lessons, but they were restless with the confinement. To entertain them Marie played the balilaika she had brought from Vladivostok, and sang. It helped to cheer everyone.

Sometimes Marie thought about being twenty-one already and yet unmarried, but if she became wealthy, she would be in a position to decide upon a husband for herself. Nikolai's face flashed through her memory. Would he still be available? How would she set about finding him? Chiding herself for day-dreaming, she set about the never-ending job of chopping wood.

Staring out the window during a moment of daylight on a clear day, Marie noticed a dogsled approaching. Ten pairs of multicolored huskies, running at full speed and effortlessly pulling a sled made of wood and leather, skimmed along the surface of snow, spewing an arc of snow in their wake. A bulky form perched precariously on the back of the sled runners, one hand holding onto the sled, the other cracking a whip above the dogs' heads.

Racing around the front of the building, the team of huskies stopped. Setting the hand brake on the dogsled, a fur-clad figure stepped off the back runners. A ruff on his parka covered his face. Cold had frozen his exhaled breath into icicles clinging to the bottom of the ruff. A round bundle rolled off the sled and stood upright, revealing a much shorter man who worked his way to the lead dogs. The two men drove stakes into the frozen snow, then tied the two lead dogs to the stake. Clouds of vapor encircled each dog's head as he dropped panting to the ground, tongue dangling. Shimmering icicles wreathed the head, whiskers, muzzle, and eyelashes. The driver and his helper then proceeded to set three more stakes at intervals to keep the dogs in place to prevent tangling and fighting.

Approaching the door, the driver knocked twice and Marie opened the door.

"Do you think a fellow could get a cup of tea?" he asked in Eskimo as he pulled off his fur gloves, slid back the hood and removed his parka.

The man's deep blue eyes studied Marie as he placed the garments into Marie's outstretched hands, brushing the snow as he did so. His hands lightly touched hers. She looked up into sparkling blue eyes that held hers as she quickly withdrew her hand. She blushed at his frank appraisal of her neatly braided chestnut hair with attractive reddish highlights. She waited for him to remove his stocking cap, but he kept it on.

He repeated the question in English. Marie still did not understand.

Just then the Eskimo companion walked through the door and was asked to translate in Russian. Marie smiled. She finally understood what was being asked.

"Of course, we have tea. You are welcome to sit while I fix something to eat and drink," Marie told the Eskimo who repeated the invitation in his own language. The Eskimoes had learned to speak Russian in school.

Meantime, Mrs. Nazarova came in from the kitchen and introduced herself. Turning to Marie she said, "This is Marie Zimina, and these two are my children with Mr. Nazarov," she added, as the two curious youngsters bounded in with their dad.

With the Eskimo translating, the driver said, "My name is Carl Johnson. I run the Sanavina trading station about twenty miles north of here. I buy furs from the Eskimoes who told me you people had moved into the school. I wanted to welcome you to Indian Bay."

After a short visit through the interpreter and a warm meal with several cups of tea, the visitors donned their parkas and gloves. Carl's thanks needed no translating. He said that he would be down that way again when he once more returned to trade for furs.

Marie watched them until the racing dogsled disappeared from sight.

The winter was unrelenting; the nights were monotonous. Mr. Cherneskow's health deteriorated.

One morning, in early spring, they found the old man dead in his bed. They asked one of the Eskimoes to dig a grave for him in the snow. There was no lumber to make a coffin, so they wrapped him in burlap sacks from the leaf tobacco bundles. They found enough driftwood to make a cross to mark the grave and said a brief prayer for the ill-fated man. Scurvy and the harsh frozen tundra claimed another victim.

How many more of their party would lose the struggle to survive in this God-forsaken environment?

CHAPTER THIRTEEN

DOGSLEDDING TO PROVIDINIYA WITH CARL JOHNSON

A loud knock on the door startled Marie. Looking up from her book she was reading to the children, she watched as Anna opened the door. A cold, icy blast of air swept over her when a sealskin-clad man stomped through the doorway shaking snow off his fur parka. The gray twilight of midday silhouetted the newcomer as he shook and wiggled like a husky after a snowstorm.

Immediately Marie recognized the parka. Carl Johnson had returned. And this time she was ready. She quickly retrieved a Russian-English dictionary from among her books and pointed out words to communicate with him.

What a welcome break in a long, long winter. She was getting cabin fever from so many days cooped up inside with the Nazarovs, the only people she had talked to all winter. True, Eskimoes had stopped to trade fresh meat for tobacco, but now the tobacco was almost gone and she had learned just a few Eskimo words.

Sitting around the warm brick stove in the kitchen drinking tea, Carl indicated by word and by using her Russian/English Dictionary, "Come with me to Providiniya. There is a trading station there that is run by a friend of mine. He and his wife are American and they have a little boy one year old."

Marie gradually grasped the message he was trying to convey. Carl continued, "It is less than thirty miles away so you will have to stay overnight with them. I have brought a parka for you to wear and fur gloves so you can stay warm."

Surprised, Marie turned to Mrs. Nazarov, "Do you think it will be all right? I would like so much to get out."

"You will enjoy the change of company. I never realized when we came here that it would be so isolated. The Eskimoes respect Mr. Johnson. I think you will be safe with him."

"Tell Mr. Johnson I would like to go with him. It will only take a few minutes to get ready."

Carl smiled. It had been a long time since he had spent any time with a white woman. There were a scant number of white women along the Siberian coast and those were married women. Standing up, Carl donned his parka and fur-lined deerskin gloves as he went out to his sled to get the winter clothing he had brought along just in case Marie was willing to accompany him.

Doubts assailed Marie as she pulled on her fur-lined, knee-length boots. Papa probably would not approve of her going alone with a strange man on an overnight trip. She decided that after everything she had been through, she could take care of herself.

Tugging the roomy sealskin parka over her head, she caught her breath as the over-powering stench of well-worn, unwashed fur assailed her nose. Once the parka was over her head, the coat didn't smell as bad.

Trudging through the snow to the waiting dogsled, Marie pulled the parka down over her face and covered her mouth with her mitten. It must be -40 degrees below zero, she thought. Carl motioned her to climb in as he lifted two thick polar bear skin robes out of the sled. Wrapping her in one rug, he tucked the second around and beneath her to prevent them from blowing off as they raced across the snow.

He quickly pulled the stakes tethering the dogs. Anticipating the journey, the impatient huskies nipped at each other and strained at the harness waiting for Carl's command. Trotting to the back of the sled, Carl raised his whip, hollered, and the twenty eager dogs lunged forward. Slick runners on the sled skimmed along the crunchy snow-covered tundra. Carl shouted again and the dogs broke into the fast run that they could hold for hours.

Marie pulled the polar bear rug over her face to break the freezing wind and to shield her face from the snow flying from under the dogs' feet. The swaying and rocking of the sled was almost like a baby's cradle rocked to and fro. The melodic swish of the snow sent flying through the air by the baleen sled runners accompanied the rhythmic beat of the huskies' feet. It reminded her of racing across the steppes at Antipina in a sleigh pulled by three horses. She wondered if she would survive to ride in a troika again. When she had dreamed of traveling, the thought never crossed her mind that her means of transportation would be a dogsled, nor that she would be stranded on the far northeastern corner of Siberia.

Marie learned that the reason the natives used baleen for the sled runners was that they did not freeze like wood or metal. When metal runners were all they had, they would dip them in water, let them freeze, re-dip until a heavy coating of ice permitted smoother travel; a single layer of ice merely clung to snow. The baleen came from the mouth of whales where it served to filter plankton and other marine invertebrates the whales ate. An Eskimo village could survive the winter on one whale harpooned by a hunting party during the summer. All parts of the whale were used. Blubber from the whale was called muktuk and was eaten raw by the Eskimoes. Extra meat was stored in a pit dug in the ever-frozen tundra.

The gray twilight gave the land an eerie, ethereal appearance. The silence of the tundra was interrupted only by the momentary swish of the sled and the huskies' breathing as they followed their lead dog, Harry. The leather harness binding each pair side by side and nose to tail combined their speed and strength to effortlessly whisk the sled over the ghostly-grey ground.

Arriving in Providiniya late that afternoon, Marie stiffly hoisted herself out of the sled. The temperature was hovering around -50 below zero. Carl unhitched his dogs and staked them separately to keep them from fighting before feeding each its rations of dried salmon that he always carried on the sled.

Mr. Thompson, operator of the trading post, answered Carl's knock.

"Well, if it isn't Carl Johnson, you old Swede! Come on in. Don't just stand there lettin' in all that cold air."

Carl turned around and ushered Marie into the warm trading post. "I brought Marie Zimina from Indian Point. I thought you folks might enjoy her company, just as I am sure she will enjoy yours. She doesn't speak English or Eskimo, so you will have to translate in Russian."

"Why you old dog, you! You didn't tell me you had a girl friend hid out on the tundra!"

Carl shook his head. "You have it all wrong. I thought your wife would enjoy her company and she needed to get away from Indian Bay for a day or two."

Not understanding a word that was said, Marie nervously looked around the crowded trading post. Mr. Thompson noticed her discomfort, "Welcome to Providiniya, Marie. I'm Thompson. I'll go get my wife so you can meet her. She will get you fixed up with a place to sleep and some grub" He spoke in fluent Russian.

"Thank you, Mr. Thompson, I am rather tired," she said as relief flooded her face upon hearing a familiar tongue.

After spending the night at the post, Carl set about taking care of the business he had come to do.

Marie felt more at ease with Mr. Thompson who not only spoke her language, but also introduced her to Pavlov, the man who had been the Russian teacher at Indian Point school. Their conversation was brief for Carl was ready to go back.

The weather was nice but very cold. The dogs traveled fast and Marie's cheeks started to freeze. Carl noticed she was trying to see everything and was not staying covered. Shouting at the dogs to halt, he knelt down by the sled and saw her frozen white cheeks. They were numb so she hadn't noticed. Motioning, he tried to explain what he was doing as he picked up snow and began to rub her face to get the circulation going. He knew well the pain that she would feel as he gently massaged, and tenderly smiled in sympathy. Her cheeks became red, and with no uncertain gestures he told her to stay covered up.

He tucked her in carefully. She recalled her father tucking her under a lap robe, just like now, when they were caught in a blizzard near the Tatar settlement. She had felt so secure and loved. She nodded her head to let Carl know she understood.

Returning to Indian Point, they found Mr. Nazarov was coming down with scurvy, the same disease that had claimed the old man's life. Carl had to return to his trading station, but he told them to make sure they all ate onions to avoid getting scurvy as well.

Just a few days later, Marie answered a knock on the door and was startled to see Mr. Pavlov smiling at her. He said that he was sure he could get her a teaching job in Providiniya. Marie had noticed Mrs. Thompson's proprietary air with Mr. Pavlov and she certainly did not know him well enough to accept his watch he offered her. He insisted she keep it, pushing it at her, and turning to leave before she could say another word, said, "I'll let you know when the job opens up. I will come back and help you move."

Thinking about teaching and the easier living, Marie had decided maybe this was what she should do. Before she could make plans and tell the Nazarovs, an Eskimo came with a note for her. It was in English and Marie laboriously decoded it with the aid of her Russian/English dictionary. The note was from Mrs. Thompson. "You leave Pavlov alone."

"Well, she certainly does not want me in Providiniya," thought Marie. She turned to the Eskimo,"You take this to Mr. Pavlov," she instructed as she handed him the watch.

Marie was glad Carl had taken her to Providiniya for a break because now she had to chop the wood, keep the fire going, try to divert the whining children, and search for more wood, which became harder to find as the ocean was frozen and none was washing ashore. When she thought things couldn't get worse, Anna Nazarov became ill.

Now Marie had to cook in addition to her other chores. The food supply was dwindling; there was no more tobacco to trade for fresh meat.

The ice was finally beginning to break up. They had spent all winter at Indian Point. It was impossible to look for gold on the snow and ice-covered beach. Marie was discouraged. All they could manage to do was survive and she wasn't sure how long they could do that.

One evening an American cutter on the way from Anadyr to Nome had passed by but were unable to land because of ice floes. But someone had walked across, leaving a sack of potatoes by the door with a note that read, "This year there will be no boat from Vladivostok. There is too much fighting going on to obtain supplies."

With no boat coming, they knew they would have to stay. "I can't stay here another year longer." thought Marie. If she left, there would be one less mouth to feed.

Anna was better now and she had mentioned the possibility of their moving to Providiniya. Marie did not feel that should be her choice because Mrs. Thompson had made it very clear in her note that Mr. Pavlov was her "close" friend and she did not appreciate the attention he was giving Marie. Later, Marie was to learn that Pavlov was the father of Mrs. Thompson's child.

Marie could see only one other option. She would try to get work at Sanavina Station with Carl Johnson even if it were just for her room and board. And it would just be until she could get back to Valdivostok.

Having made her decision Marie informed the Nazarovs and packed her personal possessions in her wooden satchel. Locating an Eskimo with an umiak (walrus skin boat) and dog team proved easier than she had expected.

She walked to the shore where the flimsy-looking umiak bobbed in the water. A long rawhide rope connected the boat to a team of harnessed Huskies on the edge of the shore. The excited, anxious Huskies were pulling at the tether lines that separated the pairs of dogs.

Several Eskimo men, women, and children climbed into the umiak with Marie. As they settled on bear rugs on the bottom of the boat, a helper pulled up the stakes holding the dogs. A sudden lurch sent Marie sprawling as the Huskies snapped the tow rope taut. Elated at being free to run, the Huskies raced along the shore towing the bouncing umiak while skilled oarsmen steered clear of the shore, rocks and floating objects.

Recovering her balance, Marie watched curiously as she saw some women throwing small bones into the ocean while chanting in Eskimo. In Russian she asked what they were doing?

"We ask for good luck on our journey," one of the women replied.

Marie prayed her own prayer as they picked up speed and the umiak hit another floating log.

Marie turned to look at Indian Point schoolhouse that was now just a speck on the horizon. The Nazarovs had been her only companions since they had left Ramon in Petropalovsk the previous summer. It seemed like ages since she had left her family in Antipina for what was supposed to be a two-week shopping trip.

The dogs settled into a steady rhythmic gait, keeping the tow rope taut. Gliding along the water, the umiak occasionally bumped into driftwood the tide washed in, jolting all the passengers.

Marie must have shown her alarm for a woman reassured her, "Do not worry, the boat will not break. Is very sturdy."

They stopped to rest the dogs, for two or three of them had eaten something that seemed to disagree with them. Leaving them tied on the beach, they rowed to an island in an inlet nearby. Puffins, cormorants and seagulls rose, protesting at their approach. The women chattered excitedly for the island was covered with nests full of eggs.

Scrambling out of the umiak, they all began eating eggs and gathering more to take with them. As she watched them devour raw eggs, some with chicks about to hatch, some even rotten, Marie could not help it. She vomited.

Covering her nose with her coat, Marie tried to mask the sulphurous, noxious odor. She crawled back into the boat with trembling knees. Soon all had clambered aboard exhilarated at their find. Marie leaned over the side trying not to look at the repulsive mess of eggs in the boat. She shuddered and closed her eyes, "Get me to shore," she prayed.

They camped on shore until the dogs recovered and went on their way.

To her disappointment Marie did not find Carl at Sanivina station. She should have sent word ahead, but now, here she was with no money and no food. All she had was her wooden satchel, her balalaika, and some crochet pieces she might trade, but who would want them here?

Three Americans were waiting at the Sanivina station for a boat that was going to Nome. They could not communicate with Marie, but an Eskimo girl who had lived in Nome for some time could speak some English and some Russian.

A Mr. Parsons had been left in charge of the post during Johnson's absence. Marie had the girl translate, "I am trying to get a job over winter. There will be no boats from Vladivostok."

Uncertain what to do, the men moved into a tent so Marie could have the cabin. Who knew when Carl would return? He was seeking a new area to start another post and no one knew how long that might take. The boat they were awaiting was going around the Arctic Sea to Wrangell Island and thence to Nome.

Marie sat alone in the cabin, dampening her crocheting with her tears and waiting for Carl to come.

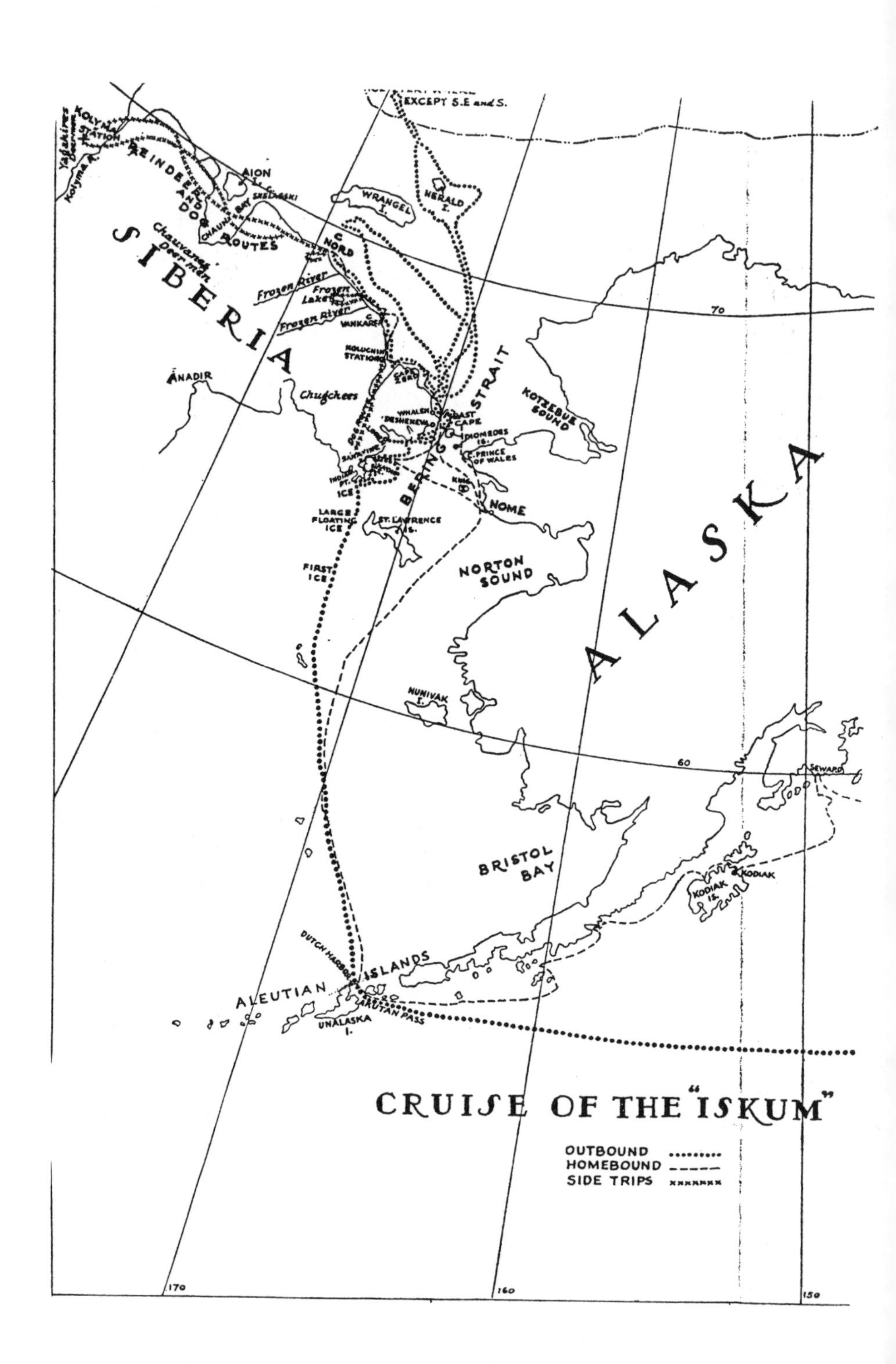
CRUISE OF THE "ISKUM"
OUTBOUND
HOMEBOUND
SIDE TRIPS
SIBERIA
ALASKA
REINDEER AND DOG ROUTES
KOLYMA STATION
Kolyma R.
AION
WRANGEL I.
HERALD I.
Chauvenes Deer men
Frozen River
Frozen Lake
VANKAREM
ANADIR
Chukchees
BERING STRAIT
EAST CAPE
KOTZEBUE SOUND
DIOMEDES IS.
C. PRINCE OF WALES
NOME
ST. LAWRENCE IS.
LARGE FLOATING ICE
FIRST ICE
NORTON SOUND
NUNIVAK I.
BRISTOL BAY
SEWARD
KODIAK
KODIAK IS.
DUTCH HARBOR
ALEUTIAN ISLANDS
AKUTAN PASS
UNALASKA I.
70
60
170
160
150

CHAPTER FOURTEEN

MARRIED AT SEA ON THE ISKUM

Shouting from outside sent Marie running to the window. The ISKUM was dropping anchor. Carl Johnson was supposed to be on board. Would he laugh at her when she asked to work for him at the trading post? Her life depended upon being able to go to work for him. Being a realist, she was aware of her desperate plight. She had no food or money and was stranded thousands of miles from home.

Nervously, she put on her wool coat and patted her hair into place. Taking a deep breath, she walked out the door of the cabin and down to the shore to meet the boat ferrying passengers and cargo to shore.

Watching the longboat intently as the rowers strained at the oars, Marie searched for Johnson's familiar face. Where is Johnson? Fingers of panic closed about her as she realized with a sinking heart that Johnson was not aboard. Struggling to maintain her composure against rising hysteria, she closed her eyes and took a deep breath.

For days she had been preparing herself for the moment when she would ask Johnson for a job. "What am I going to do now?" she wondered as she opened her eyes and watched the captain step ashore.

Feeling at a disadvantage because she could not communicate with the Americans, she frantically looked around for the Eskimo girl who had translated for her when she had arrived at the station. Spotting her, Marie motioned for her to translate.

Acting as her interpreter, the Eskimo girl asked Captain Kelly. "Where is Johnson?"

"He stayed at Koluchin Bay, northwest of here, to start a new trading post."

Upon hearing the translation, Marie felt as if her world was falling apart. What could she do without money? Her last hope was to work for Johnson and he wasn't returning.

Observing Marie's distress at hearing the news, Captain Kelly asked through the interpreter, "What is wrong?"

Marie explained her situation to the captain. Her anxious expression betrayed her dilemma. Struggling to remain calm, she turned and stared at the ISKUM gently bobbing at anchor. Slack windless canvas sails sagged against the boom just like her sagging spirit. What was to become of her? She had run out of options.

Gazing at the 67-foot long ISKUM with its vertical mast pointing skyward providing a stark contrast to the barren tundra landscape, Marie's shoulders slumped. "What am I going to do?" she asked herself. Ever since she had left Antipina she had been struggling to survive. She had always been able to draw on her inner strength to resolve her problems.

Papa had taught her to be realistic and face facts. The facts were she was a single woman alone in a hostile Siberian environment, with no money, food, or shelter and her only hope for resolving her situation had vanished with the arrival of the ISKUM at Sanavina Trading Post.

Absorbed in her inner turmoil, she slowly sank to the rocky, seashell littered beach. Sitting with her arms around her drawn up knees, she laid her forehead upon them. Overwhelmed by her situation, tears began to slide down her cheeks as she slowly rocked back and forth. Never before had she cried in public. But never before had she ever been in such a hopeless predicament.

The Iskum drying its sails.

Walking back to supervise the unloading of the longboat, Captain Kelly turned and looked at the forlorn figure huddled on the beach. Assured that supplies for the trading post were unloaded and being carried to the post, he motioned to the Eskimo girl who had served as interpreter for the young, beautiful blue-eyed girl now gazing out to sea. Together they walked over to Marie. She raised her head and stood up as they approached. Drying her tears, she brushed off her coat.

"Tell her I will be sailing today for Nome, Alaska, in the United States, and if she would like to come along, she is welcome. After we unload cargo at Nome we will be sailing for Koluchin Bay where Johnson has set up a new trading post. She can stay in Nome or go to Koluchin Bay with us."

Translating the message for Marie, the Eskimo girl watched as Marie's expression turned from hopelessness and despair to thankful.

"Tell Captain Kelly I will go with him on the ISKUM," Marie without pause, replied.

Her confidence and determination to survive strengthened as she chose this new option provided by Captain Kelly. It took only seconds to retrieve her bag and a bundle of crochet work that she could sell in Nome. So what if Nome lay just across the Bering Strait and was in a different country!

The voyage to Nome was smooth, but no one on the boat spoke Russian, so Marie kept to herself. She felt very secure in the old wooden ship, though an unknown future lay ahead.

The inside hull of the ISKUM was reinforced with iron bars and, just off the stern, railroad ties braced the hull, to protect the wooden planks from any jagged icebergs the waves might carry. The boat was powered by sails and a 75-horsepower Fairbanks-Morse oil burning engine.

The splash of the anchor alerted Marie to the fact they had arrived in Nome. Climbing the stairs to the deck, she glimpsed her first sight of the stark shoreline in the distance. The gray, weathered, wind-swept buildings, occasional tents, and make-shift dwellings dotted the beach as far as she could see. Tethered next to the houses and tents, sleddogs barked and tugged at the chains that anchored them in a row just far enough apart to prevent fighting.

In the background, the high rolling hills were green with their summer vegetation.

Because the bay was so shallow – even high tide reached a peak of only two feet – the ISKUM had anchored well off from shore. The crew lowered the dinghy that would carry her into Nome.

Captain Kelly took her to the immigration office where he introduced her to Mr. Voronisov who spoke Russian and English. The friendly officer welcomed her but had little hope of solving her immediate problem – a place to stay.

Setting forth on her own, she went to the grocery store and cafes, trying to sell her crochet work. Unfortunately, most of the eating places were part of the multitude of bars along a single street. With her limited ability to communicate, she had no luck.

Appalled by the way the woman-starved miners looked at her and made suggestive comments, she retreated. She could not understand why they acted as they did. One man volunteered, "I got a good room and a bed for two." When he became aware that Marie did not understand, he gestured the message with his hands.

As his intent became clear, Marie emphatically shook her head and snapped in Russian, "You make a mistake. I am not looking for a man to sleep with."

There were few females in Nome except for the Eskimo women. The rich gold fields had lured thousands of miners, as well as some ladies of ill-repute, to Alaska in the early 1900's. Bars in Nome had flourished off the miners' hard-earned gold. Easy pickings now long gone, some miners still persisted, hoping the beach would again yield its treasure. Others who had given up hope just did not have the money to get away from the town isolated by geographic barriers too immense to tackle. They did odd jobs and lived off whoever or whatever the sea would supply them.

Repulsed by the behavior of the men, limited by the language barrier that prevented her from selling any crochet work, she was miserable. She hated Nome.

Both Captain Kelly and Mr. Voronisov encouraged her to go to Koluchin Bay to see whether some kind of agreement could be reached with Carl Johnson. Marie agreed that would be best for her. She had never met men like those Americans; Johnson had always treated her like a gentleman! It appeared to her that her only choice was to be going back to Siberia to work for Johnson at his new trading post, if he would let her. Just as soon as she could save enough money and the war had settled down, she would return to Antipina.

On the voyage from Nome to Koluchin Bay, Mr. Kelly borrowed Marie's English/Russian dictionary and communicated the idea to Marie that Carl Johnson had shared with him on an earlier voyage that he might some day like to marry Marie. As a ship's captain, he could perform a marriage ceremony. Of course, he would have to be four miles out at sea, but he could arrange that should Marie decide that she and Carl should be married.

Marie was taken quite by surprise by the idea, but the more she thought about it, the more she began to think that her problems would be solved if she did marry Carl. She wouldn't have to worry anymore. She could work at the trading post and the arrangement would be very proper. After all, her only option at this point was to work at the trading post; she

Carl Johnson on the Iskum.

had no money for passage or food, nor a place to live. Ever since she had left Antipina she had been struggling to survive, and survive she had! If she were at home, her marriage would be arranged by the parents, but her parents were far, far away.

How would she and Carl communicate? Alarmed, Marie remembered that he did not speak Russian. What if the captain was wrong about his interest in her? Where would she be? Right back where she was now – no money, no food, no place to live.

As the ISKUM sailed northwest toward Siberia, Marie pondered her situation. She rationalized that communication between them could be achieved by using her English/Russian dictionary.

If she were committed to Carl, would Nikolai ever become a part of her future? Again she read the poem; memories of him were still so strong. Or was Nikolai now only a dream that would never happen?

Under a canopy of blue sky decorated with little puffs of white cloud, they arrived at Koluchin Bay. The gently rolling waves combined with a mild ocean breeze coaxed the ISKUM toward shore. Marie saw people coming down to the beach to meet the ship. Marie recognized Carl from a distance.

Nervously, Marie stood at the rail surveying the bleak surroundings. A newly built structure provided the only contrast to the dismal terrain. Marie scrambled into the longboat. Patting her hair and straightening her coat, she rigidly sat beside the captain.

"Hi, Carl," Captain Kelly greeted, as he jumped from the boat and reached out his hand to shake with Carl. Lowering his voice while leaning toward Carl, he explained Marie's situation and the fact that he had confided Carl's interest in her. "Look, old chap, if you are interested in getting married, you'll have to decide immediately so I can conduct the ceremony at sea before I have to sail."

Deep in thought, Carl scratched his chin. He motioned to a young Eskimo boy who had learned Russian in school. When he had trotted over, Carl told him to ask Marie to come talk with him. With the boy translating, Marie and Carl discussed marriage. They decided it would be mutually beneficial for both to marry. Within a few hours the ceremony was to take place. Marie felt relief that she would no longer have to worry about survival, but this was not how she had ever imagined her wedding would be.

So the captain took the ship out four miles from shore. The Eskimo boy and his family were witnesses as Captain Kelly read from his book and wrote a marriage certificate. Speaking only Russian, Marie Zimina pledged her vows to Carl Johnson who spoke his in English as the Eskimo boy translated words for them. Carl Johnson and Marie Zimina agree..."

The wedding party returned to shore. After coffee and a drink in the newly constructed trading post that was to be Marie's new home, the captain said his goodbyes and left.

Standing beside Carl on the beach waving good-bye to Captain

Kelly and the ISKUM crew, Marie glanced sideways at her husband. She was now a married woman! Marie Johnson! Oh, how she wished her family could be here to celebrate her wedding. On the other hand, would they approve of the decision she had made to marry a man with whom she could not even talk? She knew very little about this man standing next to her except that he was polite and he could provide her with food and shelter. That was very little upon which to base a marriage.

Trepidation flooded Marie as the ISKUM disappeared on the horizon. The reality of her situation swept over her like a cold Arctic wind. The boat would not return until next spring bringing supplies and picking up furs.

In the meantime she was stranded on the north coast of Siberia, with her Swedish-born American husband with whom she could not even talk, let alone share her feelings. What had she gotten herself into this time?

Each decision she made took her farther and farther away from home. Would she ever get back to Antipina?

Carl at Koluchin Bay with a line of prize furs.

A scene of Marie and Carl taken in 1922 in Siberia.

This photo of Marie and her "clothesline" in the background appeared in James M. Ashton's book "Icebound, a Traveler's Adventure in The Siberian Arctic" published in 1929.

CHAPTER FIFTEEN

DAILY LIFE AT KOLUCHIN BAY

Carl Johnson, a Swedish immigrant, age 46, born in 1875, was twenty-four years older than Marie. Of average height and build, Carl was a strong well-muscled man. Though Carl had lost his hair while a young man due to a genetic trait, he was a rugged, good looking man. From the first day of their marriage, Carl made it perfectly clear that woman's place was in the home and woman's work WAS woman's work. His message the day they were married that Marie translated via dictionary was absolutely clear. "I shall never wash a cup!"

Working did not bother Marie; she had worked her entire life. The Arctic summer days were twenty-four hours of daylight, and they had much work to do before late August cold weather started.

Living in the one-room trading post was awkward because visitors came day and night to get supplies and trade their furs. So, immediately the newlyweds started working on a log and sod house. Building near the trading post on the seashore, they picked up driftwood logs that the constantly moving ocean tossed up on the beach during violent storms. Since Carl had served as an apprentice stone mason in Seattle when he had first moved to the United States, he was adept at laying a good sod foundation.

Eskimoes came and went, helping them haul the logs and tie walrus skins to make a roof. Carl had obtained a much prized glass window from the boat, which allowed their cabin more light. Eskimoes made their windows out of walrus intestine, which admitted a small amount of light into their dwellings.

In a short time, the house was ready. Filling the cracks between the logs with moss they had collected, helped insulate against the Arctic cold and wind. Carl manufactured a wooden stove pipe for ventilation of smoke and fumes. Eerie, haunted, moaning sounds emanated from the chimney when the wind blew, "I yeeyeeyee." Marie hated the noise at first, because it sounded spooky, but she eventually got used to it. A canvas awning was erected over the window so the snow would be easier to clear. They need only shake the canvas to remove the snow and let in the light. In the winter there was no daylight – only light from the moon for two months with just dusky light at noon.

Working side by side with Carl to build the cabin left little time to visit because Marie had to rely on her dictionary to translate what Carl was saying. They had become adept at reading each other's hand signals.

No sooner was their cabin completed than they began a building to use for an ice house to store dog food. During the winter, food for the dogs would be hard to come by. Carl was very particular about taking care of his dogs. His life depended upon his dogs. Bit by bit, Marie learned more about Carl.

Moving to Seattle, Washington, in the early 1900's, from Sweden had been a big step for Carl. Later, two of his sisters, Charlotte and Ingrid moved from Sweden to Seattle to join him, sharing his apartment. Charlotte met and married Olaf Swenson and they moved to Polson, Montana, to homestead. Carl joined them in Polson and filed on an eighty-acre homestead near the Swensons. Less than two years later, he came

A meal is served in the one-room trading post at Koluchin Bay. Note the furs hanging in the background.

home one evening and discovered his cabin had been burned down. He sold his homestead to the Swensons and looked for further adventure.

Rumors of gold and instant wealth had drifted in from Kamchatka Peninsula on the Siberian coast. Talking Olaf Swenson into going with him, they headed to the Kamchatka fields of gold where it was rumored the gold just had to be picked up off the beaches. Disenchanted after months of grubbing for gold on the Russian coast without results, Carl drifted to the Nome, Alaska, gold fields.

While in Nome, he became involved with dogsled racing. Driving a dog team for another owner in his first race, the All Alaska Sweepstakes Race in 1910, he placed fourth. Entering his own team the following year in the same race, he placed third. Intent on winning the All Alaska Sweepstakes in 1912, he entered his Siberian husky team and again placed third. Because his Huskies were running fast and working as a team, that same year he entered them in the Solomon Derby. Racing from Nome to Solomon, he covered the 65 miles in five hours, forty-seven minutes and twenty-four seconds. His record time was not beaten for the next four years. It was while living in Nome that he became fluent in the Eskimo language.

Returning to Polson in 1918, he built a two-room cabin on his lot in Polson. On a visit to Seattle, he met James Ashton, who persuaded Carl to join his Phoenix Northern Arctic Fur Company. Carl's ability to speak

An Eskimo home in the Koluchin Bay area.

Eskimo was greatly needed to carry on trade along the Siberian Coast. Adventure lured him into accepting the job, and he had been working for the trading company ever since.

Harry, Carl's lead sleddog and constant companion was special to Carl. Harry had pulled and led Carl's sled many hundreds of miles. Worthy of a doghouse, Harry soon moved into his new residence that Carl and Marie built on the seashore not far from the trading post.

Nearby the Chuckchi had built a village. Their homes were made from poles covered with different hides – mostly caribou or walrus. Because the sea provided them generously with food, the Chuckchis were able to build permanent structures, unlike the other two groups – the Eskimo and the Deermen who must keep moving, seeking food.

Marie and Carl became friends with the natives. Marie could make out some of the children's attempts to speak the Russian they had been exposed to before all northern Siberian schools were closed. Though each native group spoke in its own dialect, Carl could manage to communicate, especially since the natives were so eager to trade.

Often Marie went with Carl on his trading rounds, traveling on the dogsled. When he stopped at a dwelling to feed the dogs, they would stay overnight. The houses were conical in shape, about twenty feet in diameter, made of driftwood and skins weighted down with stones. For further security from Arctic gales, they leaned their sleds against the windward side.

Upon entering the enclosed houses, Marie felt faint at the blast of fetid air that assailed her nostrils. House cleaning took place only twice a year and the smell of hides, meat, and unwashed bodies was almost impossible to bear. No one else appeared bothered, and she had survived worse. The people were so friendly and gracious she could not offend them.

But Marie was more appalled that they took off almost all their clothing as they came in. Generally, the children were totally naked. In the winter, the very young wore union suits with a slot left in the crotch where a pad of moss could be strapped in to serve as a diaper. Inside the hut, women wore a small piece of rag tied around their hips; their faces had tatooed designs and they wore beads around their necks. The men wore narrow trunks of sealskin.

It took some getting used to, but they were all so relaxed that Marie overcame her embarrassment and looked around with interest.

Within the dwelling there was another room covered all around with hides and skins, as was the floor. There was a small space between the outer and inner walls. This was used for storage of many items; it housed the dogs when winter storms were too severe; it also served as the family's sanitary convenience in the coldest weather.

In the middle of the room was a metal plate, maybe one foot by two feet, upon which they put the oil or moss they burned for warmth and used as a cooking surface. There was always a pot of tea. Rather than start a fresh pot each time, they would simply add more water and more tea leaves. When there was no more room in the pot, then, and only then, did they empty the pot and start again.

Carl Johnson, photo taken in 1922.

Often the Johnsons must stay the night so carried their bedrolls of fur with them. Sleeping bags from the trading post became a much desired item.

While trying to survive at Indian Point, Marie had learned to live on the subsistence diet of the Eskimoes, which was not too different from the Chuckchis. The women and children in all the native groups collected wild edible plants and roots. Early in the fall, they gathered willow leaves and stored them in the permafrosted ground, to eat like lettuce during the winter. Dwarf willow and wild sorrel were mixed with blood and fat, making a greenish pulp, a delicacy. This was cooked in special pots and when the temperature was low, it was frozen and eaten as a garnish for the meat. Walrus meat would be buried deep enough to prevent decay, but shallow enough to allow aging, as they had no salt. The meat would ferment and was eaten all winter. They ate seaweed with fat, raw or cooked. Birds were hunted with special throwing weapons unless the lucky hunter owned a gun. Ducks and geese were quietly stalked, surrounded, and killed with sticks.

While the Eskimoes at Indian Point used fish as a staple in their diet, the Chuckchis did little fishing except for halibut and cod. Before the advent of guns, harpoons were used to spear the animals. It took several parties to land a whale, which was shared by everyone. One whale could supply an entire village with meat and blubber for a year. But when guns appeared on the scene and foreign whalers could so easily kill the whales, the villagers were forced to turn to other sources of food.

Marie in the 1920s.

Individual hunters used kayaks, a single or double capacity boat; larger hunting parties used umiaks. These boats were made from walrus hide, preferably female walrus. Bulls had a bad habit of fighting and thus scarring their hides and the blemishes weakened the sides of the boat. The wooden lattice frame was bound together with leather straps. These hide boats were light and easy to handle and could withstand pressure from ice floes as they were resilient, withstood the pummeling, and did not break.

Marie wondered at the number of women in a household, but soon learned that a good Chuckchi provider could have more than one wife. The Deermen, a relative of the Eskimo, only had one wife. Marie did not know whether it was a tradition or a matter of economics – perhaps one was all he could afford.

The Deermen were so called because their lifestyle depended upon the reindeer they herded that supplied food, clothing and shelter. Living inland and forced to move almost constantly for the sparse pasturage, their homes were tents of hides spread over poles that were easily dismantled, loaded on sleds and pulled by dogs to greener pastures. At least moving so often meant their homes did not smell as bad as the Chuckchi, or even the Eskimoes, whose homes were built half underground of sod with long tunnel-like corridors and stone floors. They were semi-permanent because the Eskimoes were away gathering food for long periods at a time. It was not unusual to see a makeshift tepee along the beach made out of an upright triangle covered with deerskin thrown over boat oars, which were spread a short distance apart and tied together at the top.

Though the Deermen appeared less often at the trading post, they were great traders, having traded with the Chuckchi and Eskimoes for generations for fish and seal oil. They raided each other's deer herds and took captives whom they put to work as shepherds.

Marie noticed that these women did not tattoo their faces. By now she was accustomed to the practice and gave it no thought one way or the other. But she never got over being offended by the custom that it was courteous to offer a visiting male the charms of their women. They expected the same courtesy when they were traveling away from home. The Johnsons politely excused themselves.

Marie soon learned the advantage of the warm fur parka over her woolen coat. In the winter all natives wore two layer fur garments with the inner layer of varied type fur facing toward the skin and the outer layer made up of sealskin facing outward. This coat or parka reached to the knees. The ruff around the face was made of wolverine fur because it did not freeze with breath as other furs did in the extreme cold.. Shirts of reindeer fur were designed so wide that it was easy to pull the hands out and hold the arms closer to the body for warmth. The soles of the fur boots were made of bearded sealskin or reindeer brush (coarse furred skin under the deer's hooves.) Women's boots were like the men's, only higher. Rain gear was made from walrus intestines, tattooed, but simple. The men went bareheaded except in the coldest weather when they wore fur caps under the parka hood.

In the fall all types of natives came, wanting supplies from the trading post on credit, promising to pay when they started trapping foxes and other animals. Even though Marie and Carl had never seen a man before, they would write his name in the book and give him credit.

The natives wanted tea, tobacco, ammunition, knives, hardware, sleeping bags, candles, matches, guns, goggles, eyeglasses, phonographs, mouth organs and some other musical instruments. The women wanted beads for decorating garments and slippers, mittens, warm clothing, chocolate, molasses, thread and needles, thimbles, pins, soap, combs, gingham and flannel cloth for making parka covers.

After the long winter had started, usually around Christmas time, they would start trapping white, red, and cross foxes, lots of polar bears, as well as brown and grizzly bears, wolverine and Arctic wolves. In addition, they would bring in carved ivory, extinct mammoth tusks, hand made gloves, slippers, belts, pouches – whatever they could get to trade.

Fur was always the medium of exchange. Trading was a deliberate, slow process, requiring patience and understanding. They counted everything in terms of twenty – the number of fingers and toes.

Though there were traders of many nationalities, the Germans and Norwegians were even more prevalent than the Americans. Many had never obtained permits from the governmental headquarters at Anadyr which was too far away, and the permits were too expensive. There were even Russian traders who never bothered with the legalities. The Czar was too far away and hadn't cared so long as the furs kept coming. The slow patrol boats OMSK and TOMSK were easily avoided.

It did not take long for the natives to learn just whom they could trust. Carl Johnson was fair and the natives were open and honest with him. In their years at Koluchin Bay the natives had always made good their promises to him.

Marie always had a pot of tea on the stove ready for the natives. They would come early in the morning and remain so long as there was tea in the pot.

CHAPTER SIXTEEN

CHET IS BORN

Surveying their newly constructed sod and driftwood home with its one glass window, the ice house, and Harry's doghouse, Marie felt a sense of accomplishment. Ever since her hasty marriage to Carl, they had worked long hours to complete the structures before winter set in. It was a good thing they had been busy, building and trading, so they had little time for conversing. They had been blessed with a mild summer in 1921, and Koluchin Bay had been free of ice, allowing trading schooners and boats to stop at their trading post. All the trading goods the ISKUM had left with them were neatly organized on shelves and in separate stacks around the room.

Wrapping her coat tightly around her and looking up at the sky, she knew that summer was over and winter was setting in. Honking geese had filled the air with their mating and hatching their young all summer, but now there was silence except for the wind whistling and swirling around their dwellings, and the waves slapping the shore. Walking back to the cabin with an arm full of wood, she felt the first flakes of snow light on her cheek.

Shorter days and longer nights meant that she would be spending more time indoors sewing and tanning the hides that were to be used for clothing. Longingly she thought about her family in Antipina and the community sewing bees she used to enjoy with her sisters and neighbors. Being the only white woman in such an isolated place could make for a very long winter. She sighed as she entered their cabin. Grateful she had a roof over her head and food in her stomach, she stoked the fire and started cooking supper over the big iron plate in the middle of the room.

By Christmas, there was no daylight, and Carl was gone most of the time trading in the villages. Christmas time had always been such a happy time with her family. Marie played her balalaika and sang Christmas songs to herself because Carl was not home on Christmas. When Carl returned, she would have to tell him she suspected that she was pregnant.

Returning home from his Christmas trading trip, Carl came across a young Eskimo boy, named Altura, who was starving to death. His parents had fallen through the ice and drowned, leaving him to wander alone searching for a village. Inviting him to sleep in the trading post and work for him as an interpreter, Carl acquired a loyal helper.

Strong Arctic winds ushered in 1922 and blew incessantly all winter and on into the summer. Ice flows were trapped in the bay as the wind pushed them against the shore, creating a six-mile barrier for the ships trying to deliver supplies.

On July 7, a boat with supplies was expected from Seattle, but the ice was too jammed up to allow entrance into the bay. Carl went hunting on the ice pack with his dog team. Two Chuckchi women came by and Marie made them tea. Moving around was cumbersome because she was expecting her baby any day.

When she had told Carl that she was pregnant, he had accepted the news with indifference. Nothing more had been said about the baby that was due any day, but Marie had been making baby clothes and bedding from materials on hand, and of fur in preparation for the baby.

Scrubbing the floor on her hands and knees, Marie felt a sharp pain grip her back and abdomen. Straightening up, she took a deep breath and the pain disappeared. She knew she was going into labor. How she wished that her mother or a midwife could help her. With no one around, she was going to have to deliver her own baby. Unsettling as the truth was, she was grateful for the training that she had in the Vladivostok Hospital in the obstetrical ward.

Mopping the floor helped keep her mind off the ever increasing sharp pains. She understood now why so many women she had taken care of in the hospital screamed out with pain as their pains intensified. Breathing deeply and clutching the edge of the table she bent over, trying to relieve the vise-like gripping pain that encircled her body. Beads of sweat broke out on her forehead.

Standing up, she began to walk around the room, pausing only when wracking pain caused her to double over. Everything was in readiness for the baby's arrival. Experience in the hospital had taught her what supplies she needed, and what to do when the baby was born. Remembering some of the women who had complications with breech births and improperly positioned babies, deepened her concern because there was no doctor within hundreds of miles. If she had problems there would be no one to help her – not even Carl. She had never felt so alone in her life. Praying for strength from God, she started to sing to ease the pain.

A rush of fluid warned Marie that the baby would soon be born. Lying down on the bed, she propped up her head and shoulders so she could push with the pains. Breathing deeply between pains, she pushed as hard as she could. She felt as though her insides were being ripped out. The baby's head slid out. Reaching over her huge belly, Marie gently turned the baby's head as she had been taught to do in the hospital. She gave a mighty push; the shoulders cleared the birth canal. One more push and the baby was delivered.

Quickly, Marie pushed her exhausted body into a sitting position and lovingly picked up her newborn son. Clearing the baby boy's nose and mouth, she turned him upside down and patted him on the bottom. A lusty wail burst forth from his lungs. Flailing arms and legs made his slippery body difficult to hold. Carefully, she wrapped him in a clean blanket. Tying and severing the umbilical cord was difficult because of her shaking fingers. That completed, she laid back with the baby in her arms and held him close to her breast. Instinctively, her new baby began to suck.

Exhausted, Marie rested. Soon the afterbirth was expelled. Marie laid the sleeping infant on the bed and tiredly arose to clean up the soiled blankets. Slowly, she cleaned and dressed the baby, wrapping him in a clean blanket. Wearily, she lay down on the clean bed and cradled her newborn in her arms. Because of the twenty-four hours of daylight, she had no idea what time of day the baby was born. Marie dozed.

Awakening at the slamming of the cabin door, Marie sat up quickly, aching all over. Carl was home.

Marie held up the baby, "Our baby boy."

Carl looked at the sleeping baby and smiled.

"Let's name him Chester," Carl said. They had discussed baby names and Marie had liked the name Chester.

Looking around the room, Johnson asked, "Where's the bread?"

"I forgot to bake bread. There are some crackers."

"I don't want crackers, I want bread," he replied with irritation as he sat down in his chair, expressing his annoyance that she did not have fresh bread ready for him.

She had not realized so much of the Old Country had come from Sweden with Carl. Woman's job was to take care of her man and having babies was all in the line of duty. She should have been prepared. Marie got up immediately and started baking bread.

Carl left on a trip the day after "Chet" was born. Marie had been up on her feet too soon after the baby was born. She began hemorrhaging. A native woman came in to see the baby and Marie gestured the message that she was bleeding. The native woman helped pack her with reindeer hide strips to stop the flow. A piece of hair lodged in the tear, causing a serious infection. Running a fever from the infection Marie would probably have died had she not brought with her an ointment they had used in the Vladivostok hospital. After several days her fever broke.

When Carl had said he would never wash a cup, he meant it. Marie wondered who had washed his cups in the past. There were boxes of dishes unopened when she came.

Carl had never showed any interest in the native women, but before they had married, he had had one of them come in to mend his garments and prepare his food. Though Marie was willing to work she had not expected to be treated like a slave.

Chet was a healthy baby. Placing him under a tent of walrus hides with a kerosene lantern kept him warm. Though they had a fire in their driftwood cabin, it did not stay very warm because of the constantly blowing wind. In fact, most of the year, the underside of the ceiling was iced over.

The natives wanted to touch Chet because his skin was so white. Marie would proudly hold him up so they could see him. When Carl was home, Altura, his Eskimo helper, kept Chet occupied and assisted in his care.

Chet was only fifteen days old when James Ashton, owner of the Phoenix Northern Arctic Trading Company and Carl's boss, arrived in the company boat the ISKUM. The wind had shifted and blown all the ice pack out to sea. Mr. Ashton was curious to meet this lady he had heard so much about. He ordered the crew to unload the best provisions they had on board.

In spite of the meager accommodations, Marie was most gracious. Ashton admired the chubby, happy baby that was the first white child born in the Siberian Arctic. Distressing to Marie was the fact that she did not have the clothing for her baby like the soft fabric clothes that her brother Alexi's children wore. The hospital baby clothes had been so soft compared to the tanned hide and rough fabric garments that Chet had to wear. While accustomed to doing without for herself, she wanted better for her new baby boy. Having to make do with what she had to sew with, she hoped that someday she could provide Chet with better clothes. It was hard for her to get used to using moss for Chet's diaper.

"I am hoping that you can work it into your plans for Marie and me to move to the Kolyma Post at Chaum Bay," Carl said to Mr. Ashton as they sat at the table drinking hot tea. "The local natives have learned how to make homebrew, probably from the Russian prisoners down south at the penal colonies. My concern is for the safety of my family. Drinking natives have a tendency to become a bit savage when they are drunk. I have to be gone so much; I do worry about their safety."

"You do speak Chuckchi, and no one else aboard the ISKUM does," Ashton thoughtfully rubbed his chin. "I can leave Captain Winnerlund here to take care of this post. Does Marie want to go?"

"Yes, she does," Carl answered.

Delighted with the news, Marie started packing. She had her own reasons for wanting to move. At Kolyma there were white Russian-speaking women, some of them wives of political exiles. Half the population were Cossacks and their families.

Altura chose to travel with them to Kolyma, because they had become his family, and he had a great deal of respect for Carl, who had saved his life.

On the way up the coast, Carl was sent by Ashton to check out another possible sight at Nord for a trading post. The supply of wood on the beach was an important factor. The natives said it was about five miles, but it was closer to fifteen. Finding no wood, Carl started back. He used his penknife to pick Marie a bouquet of pink and white flowers, so short of stem they had to be cut out of the tundra.

Sailing into the Arctic Sea, they were trapped, along with several boats marooned by ice. They waited for the wind to shift the ice pack so they could move. For twelve days the ISKUM was unable to proceed, locked tight in the clutches of the grinding ice. Mr. Ashton was afraid they would have to spend the winter locked in the ice. The wind changed, causing a break in the ice pack. As soon as the ice shifted enough to move, they turned, tooted the horn to say, "Good-bye" to the other boats and escaped into open ocean.

No sooner had they escaped the ice floe, when voices screamed, "Fire! Fire! Fire!" Grabbing buckets with ropes tied to handles, every member of the crew formed a bucket brigade to douse the flames leaping from the deck, fueled by the oil soaked wood. Protecting the cargo lashed to the decks was the first priority.

Marie was petrified. There was nowhere to escape off the boat. With month-old Chet in her arms, she watched in horror as the flames seemed to spread. Within minutes, the crew contained the fire. Sparks flying from the smokestack had landed on the volatile deck.

On this occasion, the Iskum was locked in an ice pack and about to be abandoned before a change of wind saved it.

The prospects of returning to Koluchin Bay depressed Marie, and the thought of spending her third winter on the Siberian Coast was overwhelming. Having her heart set on residing at Kolyma among white Russian families had seemed almost too good to be true. It appeared that it was.

The only happy person on board was Altura. Ashton had hired him on as cabin boy.

Back at the Koluchin Bay post, their personal belongings were unloaded and furs were transferred from the post to the ISKUM. Marie reluctantly unpacked and settled in for another winter in the frozen North.

After Christmas, Carl and an Eskimo decided to travel to a neighboring station by dogsled to restock dwindling supplies. Taking two sleds and two teams, they said they should gone for only a week or so. Facing a week alone with Chet in the twenty-four hour darkness did not appeal to Marie. The temperature was fifty below zero and the howling Arctic wind seemed to never stop blowing.

After they left, the wind increased and the temperature dropped. Ice covered the inside of the walrus skin roof and upper walls. Growling like a fierce beast trying to devour them, the wind buffeted and blasted their little hut. Marie had to keep the fire burning constantly, which meant going out and collecting wood from the woodpile. Feeding the dogs Carl had left behind, was extremely hazardous. Marie had to find her way to the ice shed, then carry the dried meat to the dogs picketed eight feet apart. She knew that if she became lost in the blizzard, Chet would die.

After a week, the storm still raged on with no sign of letting up. Uneasy because Carl had not returned home, Marie felt like a prisoner. Trying to keep busy sewing mukluks and parkas, Marie understood what "cabin fever" meant. Knowing that travel was impossible in that kind of weather did not make the waiting any easier. The eternal darkness weighed like a heavy pall over Marie. Wishing she had one of her sister's icons, she said many prayers that the weather would clear.

At the end of the second week, Marie was certain that Carl must be dead. No one could survive the continual cold and wind for two weeks. They had only enough supplies to feed the dogs for a week. What would she do if Carl did not come back? She shuddered to think that she would be trapped until late June or July before a boat could reach her.

Providing for their physical needs would not be hard, since the trading post was well-stocked, but the eternal blackness, wind, isolation, and confinement were beating down her spirit. She must hold on and survive for Chet's sake.

It was with much rejoicing that Carl and his companion were welcomed home, safe and sound, when the weather improved. Marie said a prayer of thanks, as she prepared Carl's meal. The men had spent most of the two weeks holed up with their dogs in a snow bank. At times, they were certain they would perish before the blizzard stopped. They almost had; they had come much too close. The unforgiving Arctic had almost claimed two more victims. How could they stand another winter?

CHAPTER SEVENTEEN

UNDER COMMUNIST ARREST

Honking geese signaled the return of spring to the Arctic as pairs of geese claimed their territories to make nests and lay their eggs. Their arrival meant that there would be fresh eggs, roast goose, and new down pillows and sleeping bags.

As the tundra thawed, potholes of water collected and mosquitoes profusely multiplied. Tundra vegetation turned the brown barren hills green.

Lengthening days allowed Marie and Chet to be outside for longer periods of time. Chet loved it because he was just beginning to walk.

Dwellings were aired out. Furs were hung outside on racks to freshen up in the sun.

Hoping that this spring of 1923, the ISKUM would come from Seattle, Marie and Carl bundled the furs that had been traded during the winter, preparing them for transport. Every day they searched the horizon for signs of the boat.

Finally one day, a boat dropped anchor and three men rowed ashore in a longboat. Three White Russian soldiers introduced themselves and had tea and lunch with Marie and Carl. They made a fuss over Chet, who by now, was toddling around, chewing on bones that Marie had cooked. His favorite food was shark fin boiled and prepared like the pig's headcheese back home.

The soldiers gave Marie a proclamation (Protokol) in Russian to read. She translated for Carl. It explained why the ISKUM had not arrived. After being seized for illegally trading in Russian waters, the ISKUM had run away from Anadyr with a Russian guard, whom they had taken to Nome, where he could defect. For this, the soldiers had come to confiscate everything the company owned.

The governmental headquarters at Anadyr had been proclaimed Communist in 1919; all Whites appointed by Kolchak had been arrested;

all rights of American traders revoked. Forced to take whatever the Reds wanted to trade, the natives had enthusiastically participated in Kolchak's counter-revolution in January, 1920. However, the Red Guard was restored to Soviet power and firmly established in Anadyr, late in 1923. But up to that point, the Whites still controlled upper northeast Siberia.

What could the Johnsons do? They tried to explain they had worked for three years without pay, trading for white fox, cross-fox, wolverine, red fox, wolf, hair seals, and polar bear furs, as well as deerskins. It was a blow to discover now that the ISKUM would not return! What were they going to do?

The authority in charge decided that since Marie was a Russian citizen, the ban on foreign traders was not in effect. He said, "You folks stay and work till next summer and we will be able to pay you for three or four years." He went on to say that if they did not believe him, they should come meet Mr. Burikov on board the TOMSK. Sorting the furs, they gave Marie an assortment of white fox, red fox and cross-fox, as well as two polar bear hides, to help compensate them for their wages. The remaining furs were left in storage with a soldier to guard them.

Marie accompanied the soldiers to Mr. Wall's station. There she had a pleasant room assigned while they awaited the coming of the TOMSK and Mr. Burikov. Upon its arrival the next day, Mr. Burikov told Marie to go back because he had no money to pay them for their three year's work. They confiscated all Mr. Wall's furs because he was an American. His post now belonged to the Russians.

Having no choice but to return to Koluchin, Marie located an Eskimo with a dog team to pull her in a kayak along the shore the 42 miles home. When she arrived, Carl, who had been caring for Chet, was making her an ivory necklace and bracelet. When she told him of the promise to pay them for four years next summer, they decided to stay.

However, during the summer of 1923, the Communists gained control of all Siberia.

Looking out the one glass window of their cabin, Marie was shocked to see armed Communist soldiers landing their longboat. Jumping out of the boat, they descended on the trading post and the house.

"This trading post and all properties are under arrest by the People's Communist Party," the soldier in charge announced.

The White soldier who had been left guarding the furs for the Whites was shot.

Picking up Chet, Marie walked over to her bundle of furs and sat down on them, nonchalantly spreading her coat over the canvas bag containing her furs. Searching the entire cabin, the soldiers seized everything but the Johnson's few personal possessions. Never budging from her seat on the bag, Marie fought the panic rising in her. If they became aware she was hiding something, she could be executed immediately, just like the White soldier.

One of the soldiers walked up to her and reached down. Her heart was in her throat; fear was twisting her insides. She had been found out! She would have to give up her furs – maybe her life!

"What a cute little boy," he said as he took hold of Chet's hand. "I have one about his age at home. I do miss him. What is his name?"

"His name is Chester," Marie quavered.

"How old is he?"

"Fourteen months," she answered, trying to calm her nerves.

The soldier tweaked Chet on the cheek and turned to the other two searching the cabin. Picking up an assortment of goods "under arrest" the soldiers left the cabin. Marie stayed rooted to her bench of furs, too scared to move for fear they would return. She and Carl had worked hard for those furs and she had no intention of letting the Communists take them.

Rapidly loading all the furs on the longboat, the Red soldiers departed. Marie sat on her furs for a long time after the Communist ship had loaded and sailed. Her knees were shaking so badly, she wasn't sure that she could stand. Looking back on what she had just done, she couldn't believe she had endangered their lives that way. But determination had always been one of her strengths and she was determined to keep her furs.

For several days after the Communists left, stormy weather closed in and an unusual amount of floating ice for that time of year was forced by wind into the bay. The Johnsons were unaware that on September l, 1923, at 11:58 a.m., an earthquake (later named Kanto) hit Japan. One-fifth of the houses of Yokohama were washed out to sea. 143,000 people died there and elsewhere from the tremendous devastation. The 34-foot tsunami, or tidal wave, plus 1,256 aftershocks, loosened the ice packs in the far North as well. Winds and prevailing drift blocked the coastline far in excess of the usual September freeze-up.

The U.S. Coast Guard cutter BEAR slowly edged its way along the Siberian Coast. Built in 1873 in Scotland, the BEAR was not designed as an ice cutter. But it was made of sturdy oak planking six inches thick, fastened with the best Swedish iron. Australian ironwood sheathed its hull and steel plates, extending up to the water line, protected the boat as it rammed through the ice. Dubbed a "sailing battering ram" by the crew, the BEAR, with its nineteen foot draft, had to use small boats for access to the shore.

The BEAR had been transferred to the Arctic Sea in 1885 for the U.S. Cutter Service. At first designated to protect the fur seal rookeries, it became a search and rescue unit, providing transportation for scientists and natives. The skipper wore many hats – he was judge, lawyer, doctor for everything from toothaches to broken bones, serving both the crew and islanders. He also reported on the weather and ice conditions, made up charts and provided transportation for anyone in need. In 1915, the Revenue Cutter Service merged with the Life Saving Service to become the United States Coast Guard.

Built for utility, the BEAR lacked amenities. There was one bath located in the skipper's cabin. There were bunks and lockers for each member of the crew, but most preferred to sleep in hammocks. The most common complaint was food; lacking refrigeration, they tied meat to the rigging to preserve it. Supplies consisted mainly of dried goods and whatever made up the catch of the day – if any.

The BEAR had sailed from Nome, Alaska, on September 3, 1923, headed for East Cape on the coast of Siberia. Four American trading ships were being held by self-appointed Red Commissars of the Whalen District, and the furs aboard had been seized with nebulous charges of violating custom regulations of the New Soviet government. The ISKUM and BLUE SEA, which belonged to Carl's brother-in-law, Olaf Swenson, were among the four. The other two were boats out of Nome. Though the authorities were unable to take action without orders from Petrograd, three boats were eventually released. The ISKUM had managed to escape. With its diesel power, it easily outran the coal-powered Russian boats and took advantage of the revealing smoke of the OMSK and TOMSK to keep a long distance away. (The ISKUM was lost at sea in 1931 when it struck an uncharted rock. The crew, with Captain George Devinney, escaped in three dories to Atka Island where they were rescued.)

Walking along the beach with Chet on the first clear day since the Communists had left, Marie stopped to gaze out over the ice floe. Deep in thought about the seriousness of their situation, Marie noticed a black speck that looked like a bird coming closer. Was that a large bird? Marie shielded her eyes from the sun to get a better look. As the black speck drew nearer, she saw the outline of a ship.

"Do you want to go to America?" a voice boomed through a bullhorn across the ice floe.

Startled, Marie knew enough English to understand what they were asking. Without hesitation, she cupped her hands and shouted back an English word she was sure of, "Yes!"

Picking up Chet, she ran to the trading post to get Carl. Excitedly, she told Carl what she had heard and seen. It was the answer to her prayers. Carl did not want to go. He wanted to stay. He hoped the Whites would come back into power and he would get paid four years of wages.

Marie's accent may have been apparent, but the message was very clear, "You can stay! I am going! I am taking Chet with me!"

Reluctantly, Carl set about packing. It was two days before the BEAR could get close enough to load. Taking all the ivory, both carved and raw, that he had hidden and the Communists had not found, along with the few supplies the Reds had left, Carl was reluctantly ready to leave. Rolling up their fur bedding and packing her cherished possessions in her wooden satchel, Marie was prepared. Making sure her bag of furs was loaded, she took a long look at the little sod and driftwood cabin.

Without saying "Goodbye" to anyone, they climbed aboard.

Howling with hunger, Chet woke Marie out of a deep sleep. The pitching and tossing of the BEAR alarmed her as she momentarily tried to figure where she was. Then she remembered. She was on her way to America! "Shh, shh, Little One," she crooned, "We are free!"

Marie in 1921 on the northeast coast of Siberia.

CHAPTER EIGHTEEN

RESCUED BY THE BEAR

Adjusting to the pitch and roll of the BEAR, Marie was finally able to walk around the boat without grabbing on to the deck supports to keep from falling. The first night on the BEAR she slept fitfully. Reliving her past in her dreams had been exhausting. Only memories remained of the good times with her family, but the scenes of horror and struggling to survive were still vivid as well. She had awakened feeling as though she had not slept at all.

Chet was asleep and Carl was below decks resting and keeping an eye on him. Breathing in the fresh cold Arctic air, Marie looked around at the foaming, curling waves. Below decks, the air was stuffy and reeked of kerosene and sweaty bodies.

Dodging icebergs, dislodged from the Arctic ice cap by the huge earthquake, slowed their progress as they wound their way through the menacing ice floes. Danger lurked below the surface of the ocean. Just the tip of the icebergs were visible above water. Underneath the exposed tip of the iceberg lay submerged jagged, piercing fingers of ice spread outward, silently setting a deadly trap for any unsuspecting ship that may venture too close.

In spite of the danger from icebergs, Marie surprisingly felt safe. For the first time in four years, she knew where she was going – away from the bitter cold Siberian Coast and the Communists – to America.

From Carl's description, or what she could understand of it, America was warm with beautiful trees, lakes, and mountains. She hoped Carl was right. Having listened to other people's stories and chased after other people's dreams in the Kamchatka gold fields, she had nearly lost her life.

For eight days the BEAR continued south with a brief stop at Sanavina Station to check for Americans who wished to leave. Thick ice floes gave way to scattered, occasional, single icebergs dotting the blue-green surface.

Cramped quarters allowed very little exercise. Marie always carried Chet when he went above deck with her for fear he might fall overboard. Chance for survival in the frigid Arctic water was very slim. A few minutes in the icy water and a person would lose all body heat and die.

When below deck, Marie would allow Chet to toddle around. Spending more time crawling than walking because of the constantly moving deck, Chet enjoyed being free to explore his limited surroundings.

On the eighth day, September 11, 1923, land was spotted, shrouded in mist. Marie was looking forward to actually seeing a town again. One of the crew said it was Unalaska. Sailing into the bay, visibility was only about twenty-five feet above the waterline due to fog. Catching glimpses of the brown-grassy hills with no trees, Marie thought to herself, "This looks just like Siberia in the fall."

Unalaska in Aleutian Chain just south of Dutch Harbor, where the Bear brought Marie and her family in September of 1923.

As they approached the dock, Marie could see the indistinguishable shapes of buildings on the shore. Low clouds and fog, shifting with the tide and wind, gave Marie only glimpses. Raucous noises from the birds and seal rookeries never ceased, but Marie could not see the sources of the sounds.

Unalaska, Alaska, had become a stop for cutters and the shore-based headquarters for the Bering Sea Patrol. A commercial center in the Aleutian Chain in the nineteenth century, its early population never exceeded 300. Though called by several names, the name Unalaska became official in 1898. It is believed the name came from an Aleut word meaning "dwelling together harmoniously."

Tied to the dock was a larger U.S. Coast Guard Cutter, the HAIDA. Passengers were to transfer to her from the BEAR. There was no time to explore the town because the HAIDA was getting ready to deliver mail and passengers to outlying islands. Then it would head south to Seattle. They had received word the day before that the HAIDA was being withdrawn from winter service in the Arctic. Carl and Marie were welcome to join them.

The HAIDA was a new boat, 240 feet long by 39 feet wide with 16.6 feet of draft. Equipped with first-class accommodations, it was built with a turbo-electric drive. Power was transmitted from a steam driven turbine to an electrically driven propeller. It had all the latest radio equipment providing a broader range of sending and receiving messages, rather than the old radios, with spark-gap wireless transmitters and crystal receivers. Thus communications were maintained at a much greater distance with little weather interference.

Anxious to get to Seattle, Carl and Marie wasted no time in collecting their belongings and Chet, and transferring to their new quarters aboard the HAIDA.

Accommodations on the HAIDA were more spacious. There was a doctor assigned to the boat who was available to any passengers who became ill. Because they were so accustomed to eating seal, walrus, whale and seaweed, both Carl's and Marie's stomachs became upset. After several days, their stomachs adjusted to the new diet and they felt better.

Marie had long since run out of moss with which to line Chet's diaper and had to obtain some cloth from the doctor for diapers.

Fur parkas and hide clothing became too warm as they traveled further south. The nearly 2,000 mile journey took sixteen days. During that time Marie had ample time to explore the large modern cutter. Time, too, to worry about her family from whom she had heard nothing, though she had continued to write letters. She mustn't think of Nikolai. But she still carried his poem, letter, and picture in the lining of her satchel.

Arriving in Seattle on September 27, 1923, on a warm fall day, Marie was amazed at the lush green forests that surrounded the bay. The breath-taking beauty of the island-dotted inlet, combined with the warm temperature, gave Marie the impression she had just sailed into heaven. So this was America! Antipina had never been this lush and green.

Immediately upon arrival, Marie was required to go to the immigration office with an American custom's official. Chet and Carl were able to go directly to stay with his sister, Mrs. Olaf Swenson, in Seattle.

Standing in line at the immigration office, Marie was relieved that the voyage was over and the floor no longer rocked and rolled. She still felt the swaying sensation as she stood, waiting to fill out the immigration papers. Slow-moving, crowded lines, combined with too few clerks, created a bottleneck. In the middle of the night, Marie sank gratefully into a chair and fell asleep in line. By the next day, she worked her way to the front of the line and a translator helped her fill out her papers. Carl and Olaf Swenson came to see why she was delayed. Mr. Swenson talked briefly with an immigration officer, speeding up the processing of her papers. They then took her to Swenson's home.

Seattle, home of the Boeing airplane factory built in 1915 because of the abundance of spruce trees ideal for parts of airplane wings, boasted a population of 315,000 people. Seattle was founded in 1861, by a group of 24 settlers who liked the abundant forests that covered nearby mountains and islands. Logging and fishing provided a livelihood for many of the residents. Plentiful water in lakes and mountain streams offered cheap electricity. The bay was 25 to 150 fathoms deep and provided access by water. Anchorage for ships was a problem because the bays were so deep, many docks lined the shoreline. Docking in fresh water lakes that lined the bay, enabled the ocean-going ships and boats to anchor in fresh water where barnacles would die and fall off their keels.

In 1897, the first gold shipment from Alaska created a boom in Seattle shipping. It became the portal to Alaska with all freight and passengers rushing to the gold fields funneled through its gates. The town grew and flourished until a giant strike in 1919 by the IWW crippled the economy. IWW stood for Industrial Workers of the World Union, commonly known as the "Wobblies," or as the "I won't work" union. Actively associated with the Communist Party, the members went out on strike and brought Seattle's economy to a grinding halt. Seattle had not recovered from the strike before the depression set in and jobs became very scarce. It was this economic climate that Carl and Marie encountered in September, 1923.

Living with the Swensons for a week gave Marie a chance to literally get her feet on the ground and start learning American customs.

Moving into their own apartment, Carl looked for work. Skilled in the building trade, Carl found a job as a bricklayer. For three weeks he worked hard, only to be told the company had no money to pay him; they were broke. He had done all that work for nothing.

Meantime, Marie felt she must learn to speak English beyond the few words she knew. Why not work in an American home and hear and learn English at the same time? With Ingrid Romberg, another sister of Carl's, tending Chet, Marie answered an ad for a housekeeping job that paid twenty dollars a month. After the first month, Marie quit. The lady of the house spent all her time talking on the phone. How was Marie to know that in this Hebrew home they would speak only Yiddish.

Marie had an idea. Easter was coming. Thinking of the gaiety and laughter that had surrounded Easter celebrations back home and the flowers she would make to decorate the church, it occurred to her that she could make flowers to sell. Buying paper, she made all the flowers she could. Again leaving Chet with Mrs. Romberg, she went down on the Seattle waterfront to Pike's Place, the largest public market in the country where anything could be found – from a man "with tears in his eyes" grinding fresh horse radish, to fish merchants. Within a very short time, all the flowers were sold.

At the market, everyone was talking about the upcoming round-the-world flight that was going to be attempted by three U.S. Army pilots. Since moving to Seattle, Marie had many times marveled at the airplanes that flew overhead. She had not seen planes before, and now they were talking about flying three planes around the world, a distance of 26,103 miles. It would be the first time the Atlantic had been crossed via Iceland and Greenland, and the first air crossing of the China Sea. The three airplanes were the CHICAGO, piloted by Lieutenant Lowell Smith; BOSTON, piloted by Lieutenant Leigh Wade; and the NEW ORLEANS, piloted by Lieutenant Erik Henning Nelson. They were to leave Seattle on April 6, 1924. Marie was glad she was not one of them making the trip. (Two of the three planes, CHICAGO and NEW ORLEANS finished the trip of 175 days on September 28, 1924. The BOSTON was forced down due to engine trouble in the Faroe Islands in the North Atlantic. The two planes had landed 57 times and had traversed 21 countries, 25 states, and one territory, and spent 351 hours, 11 minutes flying time.)

The Phoenix Northern Trading Company paid part of the wages that were due Carl for the three years tending the trading post on the Siberian Coast, thus easing their financial worries for a time.

But Carl must find work. While he was out, Marie received her first letter from home in four years. She had written home while she was in Siberia but had never received a reply. This letter had finally caught up with her in Seattle.

Shocking news! Her father was dead! He had died one week after she had left for Vladivostok. Anna wrote, "Soviet power advanced, not all natives survived, especially Father." Papa had defied the Communists and they had executed him just as they had the White soldier guarding the furs at Koluchin Bay. "Barbara and Mother forced to go to Tyumen. Communists took horses, cows, everything. Home turned into schoolhouse. Alexi and Peter conscripted by Red army."

Sobbing, Marie sank to the floor rocking back and forth. Papa was gone! For the first eleven years of her life, she and Papa had been very close; they had always worked together. He had taught and encouraged her. Over the past four chaotic years, as she struggled to survive, her determination to live was fueled by her burning desire to get back home to Papa. Papa had been a good provider. Now the beautiful home he had built his family belonged to the Communists. All Papa had wanted was enough land of his own to grow enough crops to take care of his family so he would not have to travel nine months of the year, buying and trading. Marie's dream to return home was shattered. Papa would never see Chet. There was no home to go to anymore. She was alone with no one to comfort her. It was too much! She cried and cried.

The economy was slowing daily, providing no jobs. Watching their limited resources dwindling Marie asked Carl, "Why don't we take the train to Montana, and live in your cabin at Polson? At least there we don't have to pay rent."

Carl was reluctant to spend the money so Marie sold one of her prized polar bear hides and raised the train fare. On June 5, 1924, they loaded all their possessions on the train and headed for Montana.

Marie and Chet in Seattle, Washington, in 1923.

CHAPTER NINETEEN

MAKING A HOME AT POLSON, MONTANA

"There." Perched atop the old weather-beaten storage shed, hammer still clutched in her hand, 92-year-old Marie sat back on her heels and looked at the wind-torn shingles that she had finished tacking down. "Kids nowadays don't know beans about work," she muttered.

Frustrated, sitting in the pickup watching his grandmother, her grandson felt helpless. He had scaled the ladder with nails and hammer to repair the shed at the ranch. But before he could object, his determined grandmother scrambled up the ladder and climbed onto the roof to show him how she thought the job should be done. Had he known what to expect, he would never have volunteered to drive her the three and a half miles from her home in Polson to the ranch. But he was certain that if he did not offer, she might again try to walk the distance as she had for twenty years. She had insisted the roof must be repaired; many of her relics and valuable memories were stored in the shed below.

From her vantage point on the roof, Marie gazed around at her various properties. Not that all of her extensive land holdings could be seen from here, but she could visualize them in her mind. She knew every square foot of her properties that she had worked so hard during her lifetime to acquire through shrewd dealing. If Papa had owned this much land in Antipina, he would never have had to travel away from home many months of the year. He could have stayed at home with his family. It was his dream to own his own land. He had not lived long enough to fulfill his dream, but she had. Papa would have been proud.

Sitting down with her feet braced against the sloping roof, Marie remembered her first morning in Polson on June 8, 1924. She had opened the blinds of their hotel room window to behold a world of white. Carl's small cabin was rented so they had to stay in the old Lake Hotel until his tenants had time to relocate. During the night, a storm had blown down trees and deposited branches all over the sidewalk. As though to hide its mischief, the rain storm turned to snow, covering the damage a foot deep. Even as they watched, the trees were shedding their coats of white to expose the newly formed leaf buds of green as thawing began.

Polson, Montana, a small country town, presented a spectacular view. On the east, the rugged snow-covered Mission Mountains bounded the crystal-clear, aquamarine Flathead Lake, named for an Indian tribe in that area. It reminded her of Lake Baikal in Siberia. Polson, bordering the lake front of its south shore, nestled amidst the rolling foothills of the Rockies and the wide valleys that permitted farming.

How the town had grown since that first day when she had arrived with Carl and Chet in 1924, but much of it was visible from where she sat. Carl's two-room cabin they had moved into after two weeks, was long gone. There, Marie, again by herself, had delivered their second child, Lillian, on July 25, 1924.

Within a short time, Peter Lindquist made an offer they couldn't refuse. They were welcome to live in his house for the next two years if they would raise blue foxes from the two pairs he had purchased. Again, Carl rented out the cabin.

Sitting on the roof of the storage shed, she could still see the area where the Lindquist house stood; they had moved in on August 10, and began a venture that was to continue for years.

The house near Polson, Montana, that Carl built. It was sided with tarpaper for quite some time.

The Johnsons purchased a pair of foxes of their own from Seattle, and their fox business was underway. Carl paid five hundred dollars for his first pair, but had to pay a thousand for the second. This gave him a good start in the fox business in spite of a fiasco trying to purchase a third pair through an ad in a Seattle paper. They had to hire a lawyer to trace a bogus company from whom they had ordered a third pair of foxes. But the thousand dollars, plus lawyer's fee, was lost.

Not knowing the weather in Montana, they did not plan to pelt the foxes until January, the month preferable in Siberia. To their dismay, they learned they should have begun pelting in November. By January, the foxes were beginning to shed, so the fur was not prime. They ended up carrying the foxes another year. Pens were too crowded; at mating time, fighting foxes required constant vigilance to prevent them from killing each other.

Meantime, Carl made wooden traps and caught skunks that were so prevalent on the west shore of Flathead Lake. He pelted all the striped skunks, but kept an albino to show people. He experimented with raising marten, mink, badgers, and even coyotes at different times, but foxes became the mainstay.

When the two-year agreement with Lindquist expired, the Johnsons bought this land where Marie now sat, absorbed in memory. An eighty-acre tract was purchased from an Indian allotment through the Dixon Indian Administration Office. They paid the ten dollars an acre and set about building fox pens for what was to become the Sunny Slope Fox Farm. They dug a well and found water at seven feet.

For the family, a sixteen by sixteen foot army tent was placed on a wooden frame with boarded sides about four feet high. Packed soil provided a cold floor for the tent. The first two winters they had lived in Polson, the weather had been mild. They were sure the tent would be sufficient until they had time and money to build a more permanent structure.

That first winter swept in with a vengeance. In the tent, it was bitterly cold with lots of snow. It was not very tight. Wind pelted the tent with powdery snow that drifted in through the door flaps. Starting her day by shoveling snow out of the tent, Marie would then build a fire in the old cook stove. Next, she had to shovel a path to the fox pens to feed them and then to the barn so she could milk the cows.

Inside the tent, Marie placed the children's beds on one side of the stove and Carl's and hers on the other side. She made sleeping bags of deerskin which were very warm and probably saved their lives. Kerosene lamps provided the light. Once when told to blow out the light, Chet responded with so much gusto, his saliva blowing against the hot lantern chimney, that he shattered the glass and scared everyone. Marie thought she had left the bone-chilling cold in the Arctic when she left Koluchin Bay, but that winter she felt as though she were back in the Arctic.

Marie and Carl in 1934 with foxes they raised.

During the summer, the tent was like an oven. Marie cut her beautiful reddish-brown hair short. She saved a swatch and sighed for what could not be changed.

Adding to their problems, the foxes fought worse than dogs. Nighttime, Marie couldn't sleep for the yapping and snarling noises. She would go out and take a broom to them. Sometimes she would try putting the worst offender in a box and covering it.

"What a life!" grumbled Marie.

It became necessary to fix the pens with dividers to separate the foxes. They added an overhead about one and one-half feet wide at the top to prevent them from climbing over.

Still another problem was the lack of a fence around the place. Marie planted a garden. It came up and was doing well when the cows took over. Marie told Carl he would have to fix a fence. He refused. She planted a second time but the same thing happened. She cried and gave up.

On June 2, 1927, Marie delivered another daughter, Helen, again by herself in the tent. They were starving. Marie was so small with this pregnancy that no one knew she was in the family way. This tiny babe was no bigger than a large cooking ladle. Marie feared she would not survive, but the daughter proved just as determined as her mother, and thrived.

Carl never milked the cows; Marie got up to milk after giving birth to Helen, for there was nothing else for the children to eat. Carl had told her that if he spoiled her by doing the milking, she would always expect it. Actually Carl's hands cramped so badly from arthritis that it was extremely difficult, if not impossible, for him to milk the cows.

Carl bought a logging shack and moved it onto the property. It was to become a granary later, but for now it was an improvement on the tent, full of cracks though it was.

Marie looked across the road to the tract adjoining the highway they had bought from a man who wanted to move to Alaska. Carl put the eighty acres into wheat. The tender shoots were thick and green. The weather turned hot and dry; the wheat grew only one foot tall. Gophers wiped out what little grain survived, so they got nothing that year.

The following spring, Carl worked in that field while Chet and Lillian played nearby. One morning, Marie told Lillian to get up, but Lillian could not get up. Her legs were swollen and she could not stand. Carl got the doctor. The doctor gave Marie a prescription to fill, but it did no good. The same thing happened with a second doctor. In desperation, Marie decided to walk the three and one-half miles to town to talk with a third doctor. Carl refused to take time to drive her, saying it was useless.

Marie would not give up. This doctor was less than thrilled at seeing her so early. She explained about Lillian and the other doctors. He told her, "I'll come after breakfast."

While waiting, Marie went to the grocery store. The store owner, Walter Jensen, was most surprised to see Marie so early in the morning. She told him about Lillian, and Mr. Jensen asked for every detail.

He diagnosed, "Your daughter has a woodtick. Go home and look her hair over closely. Don't ask the doctor to go. You can do it yourself."

Marie thought about it, but the doctor had said he would pick her up so she had better wait for him and get a ride home.

On the way, Marie told the doctor what Mr. Jensen had said. Sure enough, he found the tick in the hollow in the nape of Lillian's neck. He took her to the hospital and the next morning when Marie came to visit, Lillian was running around.

Marie thanked Mr. Jensen, "You saved my little girl's life."

After that, Marie always looked for ticks on the children. But learning about ticks was to benefit the Johnsons. Marie had been buying a few cows, horses, and, especially, weaner calves at the auction. Dairies and farmers wanted milk cows but did not want to keep the calves. Marie bought the calves, fattened them in the summer, and sold them in the fall. When the cattle were infected by too many ticks they became too ill to stand. Carl and Marie pulled out the parasites, applied alcohol and saved their livestock.

After the tick scare, Carl brought loads of sawdust to put inside the fox pens. The sawdust made the foxes scratch, which spoiled their fur. They also scratched at fleas. Creosoting foxes to kill the ticks and fleas was "a big job to handle." They made large boxes in which they placed the creosote dip and then had to wrestle the unwilling animals, who resisted the smelly, unwelcome bath. Flea powder eventually took care of the problem.

On January 20, 1930, while they were living in the shack, their third daughter, Gloria, warned them she was about to make an appearance. Carl was working in the field near the highway when Marie began cramping. Walking down to the field, she told him she was starting to get sick and needed to get to town.

Carl asked, "Can't it wait?"

Marie responded, "Once it starts, you can't quit."

So Carl got the team and took Marie into town to a friend, Mrs. Swanson, as prearranged. While Carl was getting the doctor, Gloria chose to arrive. Marie again took care of the birth herself, and had the baby cleaned and dressed before Carl and the doctor got there. The doctor checked the baby and charged thirty-five dollars.

Marie was indignant, "He did nothing. I did all the work and he charged for it!"

Marie remained with Mrs. Swanson for a week and then returned to the shack with her four children. Carl did not help with the babies. He would never wake to give them a bottle. He said they would come to him if they wanted something.

Still smarting over the doctor's bill and annoyed with Carl for his seeming indifference because he did not really believe a woman was sick when she had a baby, she said, "If I had known he was like that, I would never have married him."

Marie often wondered how they managed to survive those early years. A friend of Carl's got a contract to build the bank. Carl worked for him for two days, digging the basement, when someone watching the work commented, "I see the fox man is working."

Carl quit. Too proud to ask for his pay, Marie collected the money.

Marie worked for Mrs. Thompson for one day a week, cleaning, for which she received one dollar. Mr. Thompson worked at the mill, but when he came home, he still helped his wife mop floors and do dishes. Marie would sit up all night making moccasins to sell for groceries in

Chet and Marie in 1927.

addition to her other numerous chores – cleaning, milking, tending foxes, her household work and her children. She did not think it would hurt Carl to help her out. Marie came home after watching Mr. Thompson and just sat and cried. She felt Carl could have at least helped her outside. And he never did wash a cup.

Carl complained, "Woman, you should treat me better."

Marie replied, "You treat me like a slave."

Marie resented Carl's habit of just tossing his hat when he came into the house and then expected her to find it when he needed it again. Marie had always worked hard, but in Siberia, men and women worked side-by-side. Their survival depended upon it. Years later, Marie was to realize that their differences resulted from his upbringing in Sweden. He was simply treating her like the women he had known in his youth were accustomed to being treated. And by now, Carl was in his fifties and no longer a vigorous youth.

Carl did work on an addition to a building for one week for which he was paid sixty dollars. Marie was so glad. For the first time he had brought in some money during this trying period and she did not have to make slippers to pay bills for a while.

The slippers that Marie made were of different kinds and sizes – men's women's, and children's – from the furs she had brought with her that the White Russians had given them for a bonus. Marie would sew until she was so exhausted, she fell asleep in her chair. She would wake with a start and sew some more.

Work, work was all she had ever done. And no one ever again called her, "Lazy!"

This undated photo shows Carl and Marie and children feeding fox pups on the porch of their house. At left are two of their children, Chet and Lillian.

CHAPTER TWENTY

CARL SUCCUMBS TO TUBERCULOSIS

Glancing across the driveway at the house they had started to build in 1931, Marie remembered how happy she had been when they finally sold their first foxes and could afford to buy building materials. Mr. Lewis had come from Kalispell and bought all of their blue fox pups for $5,000. Carl hired Mr. Rainey to help him build the house. Marie hired a woman to help her with the cooking so she could take care of the chores. Carl considered this an unnecessary expense, but for the first time, Marie felt like she would be able to get all her work done, since Carl never helped with the chores.

They bought silver, black, and platinum foxes and acquired other fur-bearing animals as well. Marie always knew when a fox got loose by the squawking of the chickens and the commotion in the chicken house. The foxes were so tame that they would follow her when she called to them with a bucket of horse meat in her hands.

Their money ran out before their house was finished. The inside was complete, but the outside was just tarpaper.

Shortly after moving into the house, one evening while eating dinner, three Indians rode up. Marie invited them to eat and they left right after eating. Marie thought it rather odd when one rode toward the highway while the other two went north above the house. Why did they split up?

Turning to Carl, she said, "They're up to no good."

"You're crazy. They are okay," he belittled her comment.

Marie had purchased a horse for five dollars and had the bill of sale to prove her purchase. But when Carl rode to the upper pasture the next morning, not only was the new horse gone – so were all the others, except one. The neighbors reported the one horse had given three men so much trouble, they had let down the fence to an adjoining pasture and driven the horse in there.

They knew that the horses had to have been driven north or they would have seen them from their house. So Carl and Marie headed for Big Arm after Marie's "I told you so!"

Actually the Indians had only wanted the one horse back but they couldn't separate it from the rest, so took them all. On the way the Johnsons began to meet their horses straggling back home. And in Big Arm there was their missing horse in a corral. The mane and tail had been trimmed so it wouldn't be recognized. Among the group of men on the far side of the corral were the three Indians who had eaten with them.

She marched up to them. "You pay me back my money or I am going to sheriff."

Marie had faced a lot worse threat than three Indians. They were glad to pay her back and get her out of their hair.

That winter the sky was still gray and overcast, but the blizzard had blown itself out. A band of Indians rode in with a small bunch of horses in their midst. The Johnsons were most uneasy but Carl tried to reassure them.

"They are probably wild horses and they just want to sell them," he guessed.

Looking closer, he saw the horses were his own and they obviously had drifted away during the storm. He hoped the brands would show up under longer, shaggy winter coats.

The Indians apparently believed him and a much relieved Marie invited them to come in and eat. They sat around the wood stove while she prepared the food. Carl and the leader, whom they were to learn later was Lasso Stasso, had a friendly conversation with a few words and much sign language, apparently discussing current news and, probably, the miserable weather.

Before they left Carl thanked them and paid them for their trouble. They rode off with ease and dignity.

Discovering her fifth child was on the way, Marie felt she had enough children. Barely having enough to feed and care for the children she already had, distressed Marie. Faced with another pregnancy, she despaired over her situation. She was already getting up at 4:30 every morning and usually fell asleep in her chair at night working on sewing items for sale and for the children. When would she have time to care for a new baby?

She recalled hearing somewhere that a sudden jolt could cause a woman to miscarry. Desperate, she climbed the ladder to the pigpen roof. She looked down at the ground, seven feet below. She just couldn't find time to care for another baby with her already over-loaded schedule. Decision made, she jumped off the roof to the hard ground. Landing on her back, she rolled over on her side. Lying there with the wind knocked out of her, she contemplated what she had just done. The only result of her jump was several days of sore muscles.

Months later she became ill while working with the foxes. The baby was coming. She felt so bad, she had to lie down. When the girls called her to come eat, she gasped, "I can't."

Marie just knew she was going to die. Carl and the girls kept insisting that she let them call a doctor. She kept telling them, "Just wait awhile."

If they got a doctor, they would have to pay him the $35 they didn't have. She would rather die. Hours passed by. The pains were intense, but her water would not break. Marie knew from past experience at the hospital in Vladivostok that the membrane would have to be ruptured. She reached in, trying to tear the placenta, but her fingers were too short. Carl stayed right with her, but had no idea how to help. By the time she was almost totally exhausted, the water finally broke and she started to deliver her baby boy. Fortunately, the head was coming the right way for the baby was so large, they both might not have made it. For the last time, she delivered her own baby.

Carl sat and held his second son. The girls were thrilled to go to school the next day and brag about their new brother, Gene, born on October 4, 1937.

The next day Marie was up mopping floors and doing chores.

"So many years ago," thought Marie as she turned to gaze at the spot where the Sunny Slope school house stood before it burned. Four of her children had attended that school and in those early years, they had walked the half mile home for lunch because she had nothing to send with them. Many a lunch consisted of a gruel made from ground rye – just as was breakfast, and sometimes, dinner.

The school was a typical country school with twenty to thirty students in all grades taught by one teacher who was expected to maintain the building, build the fires, and teach a well-rounded curriculum. In the winter, the students gathered around a large wood stove to keep warm. The Johnsons walked to school, although some pupils, who lived quite far away, rode horseback, and kept their horses in a red barn near the school.

Classes started with the teacher ringing the bell. Generally, all went well, but at times older boys would make it difficult for the female teachers. Once Marie was appalled to hear about a large girl, who was somewhat strange, getting into a physical fight with the teacher in front of other students. Surely the girl must know how valuable education was!

But on the whole, Marie was pleased that her children were

learning the basic subjects and such things as handwriting, art appreciation and music – one time they even had a rhythm band.

Marie felt nothing should interfere with education for her children, "No one knows what will happen and you have to be able to support yourself," she always told them.

Friday night might find the children getting home late from school; presumably, they had stayed to help clean but actually, they wanted to hear their teacher's husband play the guitar and sing while he waited for his wife to close up to go home for the week-end.

The school was a social center and often the programs were followed by dancing with music supplied by young men around the area. Carl enjoyed dancing, and as Marie sat watching, she wished she had learned to dance when she was younger. She was too proud to learn with others watching now.

A month before Christmas, the students started practicing for the program of poems, music, and plays. Sheets were strung up for curtains. One enactment of "Twas the Night Before Christmas," made a big hit, especially when Santa handed out oranges – the only ones the Johnsons, and many other children, had all year.

By the time Gene started school, a bus came by the highway and he went to school in Polson. Marie could no longer rent to tenants the small house on her forty acres that adjoined the school; no longer did the teachers pay room and board to help defray the five dollar per month rental fee.

Marie rarely attended church; there were too many demands on her time at home. She made it sound exciting for the children when she started them at the Lutheran Sunday School. The girls sang in the choir for the regular services. They walked to church every Sunday whether it was blizzarding or not. Waiting for them at home, Marie always had the house scrubbed spick-and-span and a good hot meal of fried chicken, though she hated having to kill the chickens the night before. She always loved all animals.

Marie had a deep faith in God, remembering her father had promised her to God when she was so ill. She always believed God would help, but the burden of survival for herself and her family was up to her.

But Marie did manage to find time for the programs and baptisms. Christmas, of course, was special. Marie only smiled and hugged Helen when she became so frightened that she cried while singing at a Christmas program. Each year when the program was finished, Carl would drive his team of white horses and sleigh around for them to see all the lighted trees in the yards, and, especially, the house with the big blue star on the roof. On one of those trips, Lillian almost froze her feet as she sat in the back of the sleigh dangling them over the edge. All she wanted was to get home and warm her feet.

Sunday was visiting day and usually someone dropped in. Carl and Marie were most hospitable and people were always welcome. Often the big round table in the living room was filled by friends or the curious who had heard about the "Fox Lady" and had wanted to see her collection of ivory and furs she had brought from Siberia.

Marie treated any stranger with gracious hospitality. Carl liked to visit with everyone, as well, although he preferred telling stories with old friends, some of whom had come from Sweden just has he had.

There were some who came to rent horses to ride or to discuss business. The trading skills Papa had taught Marie were put into practice. After one shrewd land trade, Carl asked Marie, "Why do they always come to you?"

Marie's response, "Why don't you ask them?"

It was not long after the house was built that Carl helped the Thompsons thresh their grain. It was hot work hauling the wheat bundles and Mr. Thompson brought the crew some ice cold beer. Marie felt the overheating and the chilling from the beer caused Carl to get pneumonia. He came home ill, but refused to see a doctor.

Carl had no faith in doctors, but he finally consented to go to two Swedish chiropractors who attended the Lutheran Church. At first, he went every week for a treatment, but started getting weaker, so he went every day. When he became so weak he could barely walk, Marie insisted, "We are going to take you to a doctor!"

Chet, now thirteen, was able to drive their old car and took Carl in to a doctor who gave them the bad news: Carl had tuberculosis!

(Gloria was seven years old. Her favorite place was on a pillow under the table close to the wood stove. Once, apparently forgotten, she was almost asleep when she heard her parents. They were going over business papers and the voices changed. Marie was crying and talking about losing the farm. Both seemed discouraged. Gloria wondered what was happening, but knew that with both parents everything would be okay. Half awake she didn't know whether the problem was the Depression, the low prices, the prairie fire that had burned their pastureland, or it was because they had just learned of Carl's disease for which there seemed to be no cure except fresh air, good food, and sunshine.)

At home, Carl rested a lot; Marie arranged for him to be in the sun in front of the window, with plenty of fresh air, but no draft. Once a tent was set up in the living room with hot stones in a tub over which water was poured, trying to relieve his congestion. The children were warned not to get too close; at that time, tuberculosis was not understood. But Carl liked to hear them tell what had gone on in school.

Marie tried to protect the children. From her vantage point on the roof, ninety-two-year-old Marie looked over at the knoll, just north of the house, where she had placed a large tent in which the children slept. They did stay well, so perhaps the fresh air helped.

Finally, the doctor, who took good care of the children and tested then often, decided it would be safer for them if Carl went to the state hospital in Galen, Montana, where they might be able to do something for him.

Chet drove the old car the 150 miles to the hospital where they heard the sad news. The tuberculosis was terminal; it had gone on too long.

That summer, Marie arranged a mattress in their pickup and Chet, with the girls riding in the back, drove to visit Carl. They brought their own food and drink, for Marie would never spend the money in restaurants. The most she would give them, and only after much begging, was a five-cent ice cream cone. They stopped at water fountains along the road. They did not stay over night so it made a very long trip.

Carl would be sitting in the yard, waiting for them. That summer was the last time the girls saw him. Just after Christmas, Marie received word Carl was asking for her. Chet drove her over. For two days Marie sat in a chair beside his bed waiting for him to rouse and talk to her. He never regained consciousness so she never knew whether he was aware of her or not. On January 24, 1939, Carl died.

None of his family was able to come to the funeral; friends from Polson came, paid their respects, and she was left alone with her five children.

The neighbors brought boxes of clothes. A Swedish friend gave Marie some money, saying he knew it was going to be hard but that was all he had to give. However, whenever they visited him in Polson, he would give them large sacks of vegetables.

A year later, Marie received a beautiful cross-stitched sampler from his sister in Denmark. Marie learned that Carl's mother had died two years previously and a sister died shortly after Carl, both from tuberculosis.

CHAPTER TWENTY- ONE

STRUGGLE TO SURVIVE

For the year while Carl had been in Galen, Marie had not felt entirely alone. True, she had to carry the responsibility, but now her children depended entirely upon her.

Marie changed. There were no more social occasions for her, no yearly picnics, or meetings with the Sunny Side Women's Club. She no longer stayed by the women at school gatherings. She sat near the men, listening to their talk about farming, when to put in crops, which crop was best for the different soils.

She decided to switch entirely to cattle from raising grain, which had taken more labor. She had to have a crash course in raising cattle, including: diseases of cattle, marketing, feeding, day-to-day care and buying. All emphasis was on preserving money, saving the farm, and paying off the mortgage. Papa had always told her that if he had owned land he could be home more and be able to make a living for his family.

All her life she had worn nothing but dresses; now she switched to pants for more comfort while working at a run. She left the house early in the morning to ride the range and check for new-born calves, for any cows that may need doctoring, build and mend fences, and make sure everything was in order.

She did the milking in the morning and the children milked in the evening. She left the family a pot of oatmeal for breakfast. They hadn't the heart to tell her it was cold and hard by the time they got up, but they knew she was thinking about them.

During the Depression, people with families could work and get ten dollars for groceries. Marie went to the government office many times to see if she could just work a day or two.

She was told, "No, you have the foxes."

She replied, "I have to get scraps that I pick up from the garbage cans and the butcher to feed my family and to stay alive. I trap gophers to feed the foxes. I can't sell pelts, because nobody is buying."

Marie and the girls would go behind the Safeway Store and sort through the garbage, supposedly for the foxes, but more than one find ended up on the table.

Desperate, Marie went once again to the government agent. He said, "You got me. What can you do?"

There was nothing available but road work which was impossible for Marie to do under the circumstances. Again the children came home for lunches of mush; after school, they had a snack of milk and biscuits. And again mush for supper. They began crying because they wanted something different.

It was critical she do something. Marie worked for two days, housecleaning, and was paid with lots of potatoes and a box of apples, most of which were rotten.

When Carl had become so ill, he had signed his share of the property over to Marie. The period after his death was a struggle for mere existence. It was urgent she come up with something.

Deciding on a plan of action, she needed to borrow money to buy calves for a few dollars at the spring auction. She would fatten them on that part of her land good for grazing, and then sell them in the fall.

Marie walked the three and one-half miles to the Polson bank with seventeen-month-old Gene in a packsack on her back, like the Siberian natives carried their young. The idea had not yet caught on in America, but the fact that people stared and laughed at her did not daunt Marie at all.

The refusal of the Polson banker to loan her money stung her pride, but not her determination. She set out walking to Ronan, a distance of fifteen miles. Talking to the banker there resulted in a relationship that was to continue for years, with the bank financing the purchase of the calves, and reaping the benefits along with Marie in the fall. So far had mutual trust developed, that in later years she went to the auctions with a check signed by the banker with the amount of purchase left blank for Marie to fill in when she completed the buy. She always made a profit for both.

Marie had several horses she would rent to people who wanted to ride around Flathead Lake or the hills above the ranch. One day, three men came to rent horses, and, as usual, Marie got the horses ready. After paying her a few dollars, they asked her to meet them at the Salish Hotel in Polson, to discuss business.

Chet accompanied her. The men were interested in acquiring land around Polson to start a resort close to Flathead Lake. They wanted Chet and Marie to buy the land with the money they would supply for the purchase, plus a commission for Marie. Marie arranged for the purchase, giving the owner a down payment for his forty acres. She also arranged to purchase Little Bull Island. Papers were drawn up to form a corporation and the men left.

The intent of the three men turned out to be somewhat shady, but a local man found others who were interested and the Bull Island went through for $2,000. (The new owner sold for $6,000, and later the island again sold for $15,000.) All Marie got for her efforts was a new coal oil lamp and $100.

From her rooftop, Marie could see the point jutting out into Polson Bay. The absentee owner of this 280-acre lakeshore property lived in New York. She contacted Marie to tell her she needed the money immediately for her brother's funeral expenses. Marie did not have the $1,500. She offered a man, known to invest in various enterprises, the collateral of her 80-acre field and two pigs. He was not interested.

Marie went to every businessman in Polson trying to borrow money. She even knocked on doors, saying, "I would like to talk to you

Fixing fence on the property where Marie raised and pastured horses.

Marie training a colt.

about money for this land that goes down to the lake."

At one stop, they shut the door in her face, refusing to talk to her. One party was sufficiently interested to call the assessor, but again a refusal.

She waited until after school was out to call on another who curtly informed her the land was worthless and she was crazy with five kids to support to even consider it.

It was getting dark as Marie walked up and down the streets. Chet was now out of school so, in desperation, she had Chet drive her out to the Kerr dam site, where she had learned a man who worked there sometimes loaned money. He listened and said he would get right back to her. Three, four days went by, and no word.

Approaching the man's wife who worked in a local store, Marie was told, "No chance."

Marie had wasted all that time waiting. She cried. It looked hopeless.

Marie had two pigs to sell, and it was time to pay the $40 per year on the 80 acres. Chet was going to a track meet in Missoula so Marie went along to sell the pigs at Daily's meat processing plant. Marie had had previous dealings there, and told a man she knew there about her problem, raising money to buy the land on Flathead Lake, concluding with, "I will make it if I have to work all 24 hours. If I have to sell the back of my skirt, I will make it!"

The man with whom she had talked did not have the money but knew someone who might help. He introduced her with, "I advise you to loan this lady the money because she will do what she says. She will make it!"

Marie was told, "Go home. In three days I will send the man who loans money from the bank. He will be there Wednesday. You round up your horses and cattle to show him. He will check up and in a week you will have your money."

As soon as the check came, Marie sent it to New York and back came the deed, abstract, everything. Later, while walking with Helen and Gloria in town, she met the wife of the man at the dam who had raised her hopes and then let her down.

Marie said, "I got the land."

"You didn't get the deed, did you?"

"Oh, yes, I did."

The woman about fainted. The owner of the shop where the woman worked later told Marie that those folks had wanted the land themselves. "You got ahead of them."

The woman shortly thereafter dropped dead of a heart attack. Marie explained, "I don't know what happened. I never had the time to find out."

With the building of the dam completed, many people left town and wanted to sell their land to someone they knew. With Marie's land adjoining theirs, she was the logical choice. Sometimes she was able to buy and sometimes not. She ended up with a lot of land that needed the old homestead fences removed and a lot more fencing to do. By 1942, she had a mile of lakeshore property on Flathead Lake.

In addition to buying land, Marie started to buy old houses, remodel them and then sell them at, of course, a profit. She bought sixty lots in Polson, developed a subdivision, putting in wells and streets. She named it the Sunrise Estates and proceeded to sell lots, though some she gave away, and again made good money. She bought an old house in town, built an addition, renting the upstairs and living in the downstairs after she retired from the ranch.

Acquiring more pasture land was her goal, usually achieved by buying in 80-acre increments. She paid the taxes on 600 acres at the top of her hill that belonged to the Federal Land Bank. It cost her three dollars an acre.

Though she could not see the property from where she sat on the roof, she recalled the summer of 1947 when a very excited neighbor came to her house saying, "Your land is dropping."

Marie could not understand what he meant. Saddling and mounting a horse, she rode to the lake. Broken poles and posts lay scattered like a handful of pick-up sticks where the ground had dropped out from under the corral. It looked like there had been an earthquake. A large pine tree had slid from her property to another's land. Riding across the road to the top of the hill, she saw a stream of water running down the hill till it came to a pile of rocks where the stream disappeared. Dismounting she climbed down to investigate. There was a big tree branch stuck in the culvert under the road. The ground was sandy and a big tunnel had washed out. Heavy rains had caused severe erosion. Marie saw at once that the underground water had caused the land to become what appeared a series of steps with cracks in between. A small cabin she owned was in jeopardy of being swallowed up by the sinking ground. She immediately brought in a dozer. Contours were carved to prevent additional erosion.

The Sunny Slope clubhouse, which sat on land donated by Marie in 1951, to the Polson Women's Club and which she had helped build, was not visible from where she sat.

Marie feeding horses in the winter.

She said, "People looked at me funny because I don't speak good English and I don't have time to study. Just pick up words here and there. They looked down on me. I gave some land to the women's club. I don't know why. Maybe that was crazy. I helped build the clubhouse, but they didn't invite me to some doings."

But at the tenth anniversary, in 1961, they changed the name of the club from Sunny Slope Club to Masumola Club – MA for Marie, SU for Sunny Slope, and LA for lake. Though Marie was honored, she never felt like a member of the society; she always felt like an outsider because of the way people treated her.

Marie modestly summed up her land deals, "I bought when land was cheap, I bought many pieces, mostly 80-acres at a time. In a few years the price would go up. I did make a good profit, buying and selling land."

She had learned well from Papa.

Marie.

CHAPTER TWENTY-TWO

MAKING DO – RAISING FOXES AND HORSES

For sixteen years after Carl died, Marie continued to raise foxes. How the children detested the foxes. They yelped at night; they kept trying to get out; they fought; mostly, they were just too much work! Marie would drive a horse and buggy to the slaughterhouse for scraps. The children helped Marie feed and water the foxes. They sorted through garbage cans in town searching for edible scraps of food.

Trapping gophers was a gruesome task, because the vise-like jaws of the steel traps only caught the gophers. Killing the gophers by hitting them over the head with a rock was repulsive to the girls, but bullets cost too much. There was a plus with the gophers, the government offered a bonus of one cent for each gopher tail turned in to their agent. The burrowing prairie dogs had invaded cropland and pastureland by the thousands and the bounty was an incentive to trap these pesky creatures. Oh how the foxes liked the meat!

Many nights the evening air hung heavy with the stench of cooking gopher and horse meat. Marie was up very late many nights chopping meat on the blocks in the meathouse for the foxes. Much of the meat was from old horses she bought for five dollars each. They had to be killed, skinned, and cut up. She cooked all the meat from the gophers, cattle tripe, and horses in a big round boiler in the house.

Lured by the putrid smell, flies swarmed into the house. By morning the ceiling was black with buzzing, swarming flies. Marie sprayed and swept them down before she cooked breakfast for the children.

By December, the foxes' pelts were thick and full and at their prime for use as coats and collars. In order to harvest the pelts without imparting any blemishes on the pelt, a fox was herded into a small air-tight box and gassed with carbon dioxide from the tail pipe of the old truck. Carl had either shot or gassed the foxes, but now Marie or Chet had the unpleasant task. Marie hated killing any animals, but their livelihood came from the fox pelts.

In this photo taken in 1944, Marie displays some of the pelts from foxes they raised.

Marie skinned and stretched the pelts over frames in preparation for tanning. During the winter, the fetid slightly rancid odor of curing furs permeated every room in the tightly closed up house. As the furs cured, the smell became more bearable.

Finally, in 1955, Marie sold all her foxes. Again she proved her business acumen. Some of the buyers did not realize that her inability to speak English well had nothing to do with her intelligence. One customer in particular, a Mr. Hall, wanted to buy, but he didn't want to pay.

"You want me to get a lawyer to make out papers?" she asked. He didn't. He paid.

With the foxes out of the way Marie felt free to take her first vacation in thirty-five years. She spent a month in California visiting her daughter, Helen, and family, as well as friends and other relatives. Then back to the farm to concentrate on raising cattle.

There had always been a lot of work to do on the farm. While Carl was still alive, they hired men to help with the field work. Especially during the depression, some would wander in from the highway looking for work. They were paid thirty dollars a month and their room and board. They stayed in a bunkhouse near the house. Some of them were a little strange.

Two sheepherders dropped in once a year and stayed a while. One was named Archie. He was tall, bright, and likeable, but a terrible alcoholic. When alcohol was unavailable, he would find flavoring extracts or anything he could, to drink. Marie took care of him during his bad times. Archie would kid Gene when he was small about having a cowboy outfit on, but hiding under a wagon when the cows came in off the range. He donned a fur coat and played Santa for Gene, even though he was drunk. He got Gene to sing "Jingle Bells" for him.

Spring and fall cattle round-ups were a social event as well as hard work. All the neighbors rode their horses over to Johnson's and they split up into teams. Each team rounded up all the cattle in a specific area and herded them into the corrals. After all the cattle were corraled, all the calves were roped and branded, and the bull calves were castrated, turning them into steers. Calves big enough to sell were separated from the main herd and kept in the corral when the rest of the cattle were moved back out onto the range.

Rounding up the horse herds was a little trickier, because each herd was led by a protective stallion that did not want his mares moved anywhere unless he was leading them. Intruders were challenged by the powerful stallions, and if it were not for the ropes the riders swung over their heads and the hollering, the stallions would fight the horses they were riding.

After the horses were rounded up, the fillies were branded and the colts were branded and castrated. After Carl died, this chore fell to Chet. Marie and Chet would discuss the merits of each colt and decide which colts would be kept as stallions. Some of the two-year-old colts would be sorted out and kept at the house to be saddle broke.

Chet learned a lot about farming by listening to the farmers talk about which grains were producing the best crops and were less susceptible to disease, which grains were bringing the most on the market and many other tips to improve their crop production. One year his eighty acres produced more wheat than any acreage around him. He was proud of his achievements. High school friends from Polson came out to ride horses and help him. Chet did not do much with his sisters – he was generally to be found underneath a car or working on a piece of equipment when he wasn't riding with his friends.

Chet went to Spokane to obtain his citizenship papers. The judge looked over his papers and said, "Since you were the first white child born on the Siberian Arctic Circle, you can have citizenship to any country in the world. Which country do you want?"

"I'd like to be a citizen of the United States."

And that was what he got. Marie had obtained her citizenship in 1939.

Marie carried baby Gene around on a packboard wherever she went, while working. She would place him in the shade and get on with her work. When he was almost five years old, the family was crushed when Dr. Dimond said Gene had to have his tonsils out, but they couldn't get the fever down. Gene was very thin and not well. They were afraid he also had tuberculosis. The doctor said it would be best to send him to the Galen Tuberculosis Center. To their great relief, his fever came down after a two-month stay, during which time Lillian and Helen rode the bus to visit him.

Back to the daily chores that were tedious, but necessary. While Marie worked from early morning through dark, the children helped feed the animals, and milked cows. They chopped wood for the big wood stove that had a big reservoir to heat the water that had to be hauled from the well. Years later, a pump was installed in the house. Kerosene lamps had to be filled, wicks trimmed, and chimneys cleaned.

Everything on the farm was used. Nothing went to waste. And most things were made from scratch. Soap was made from ash, lye, and lard, and boiled in a huge kettle outside. Milk was put into a hand separator to separate the cream from the skim milk. The cream was used to make butter. The Polson Creamery bought cream and butter when there was some to sell.

As well as the milk products, the Johnsons had their own chickens, meat and eggs. When a pig was butchered, Marie made head cheese lunch meat that had once been Carl's favorite and now the whole family enjoyed.

When the children were older, Marie again tried gardening in the hard, clay soil. Water was a problem. Marie had heard that planting potatoes by the light of the moon made for a better crop. Loading a wheelbarrow with the cut potato seed, Marie, Helen, and Lillian planted by lantern light while Gloria took care of Gene. Evidently the results were disappointing for they never tried it again.

Each spring was "kalsomine" or white-wash time for the house interior; rugs were taken out to be beaten on the clothes line and everyone helped decide which pastel color each room would be painted.

Summer was canning time. There were apple and cherry trees on the hill from which they made apple butter and sauce that was stored in the rock-lined basement. Meat and milk products were stored in the ice house. In winter, Carl had cut ice from the lake which he placed in a dug out area and covered the ice with sawdust to prevent melting. The practice continued until they were able to install a refrigerator.

Dandelions were picked and made into wine. Home-brewed beer was made in a large crock, for the men working in the fields.

The children thought the haying and threshing times were exciting, even though it entailed their pitching in. Chet would mow; Lillian would rake; Helen would be on top of the stack; Gloria rode on the rake. They took great pride in making a stack that wouldn't fall over. Usually a neighbor, Roy Bland, worked for Marie during the haying. After work everyone would climb on his Model A and go to the lake for a swim – except Marie. She was busy preparing supper. She took running the farm very seriously and took no time out for fun. After a refreshing swim, everyone was ready for dinner, especially for Marie's mouth-watering, yellow dinner rolls which were famous. Made out of eggs, butter, cream, flour and yeast, the light, fluffy rolls quickly disappeared at every meal.

Threshing was fun, too, to the children because all the neighboring men made up the threshing crews and went from farm to farm. All the women made the most wonderful food, including banana cream and lemon pies.

Lillian did a lot of cooking, watching over the younger ones, and helping with the business papers. Marie's education in Russian grammar, letter formation, and spelling only added to her confusion and caused great consternation when she tried to compose letters. To Marie, English made no sense at all. Math was understandable. But as each girl grew older, she took over the writing of business letters at Marie's dictation. Marie developed a most unique filing system. She had papers everywhere and when it came to finding things, would mutter, "Help me find paper. Gotta be somewhere! Got no legs! Can't run away!"

The children liked any work connected with riding horses. Much of their lives centered around horses. When the girls were young, they had a horse named Junior, that was so tame they could slide over its back, crawl under it and all three girls could ride him at the same time.

One of the mares that Carl had purchased, gave birth to a small, weak, coal-black colt with a white star on its forehead. Lillian spent hours working with him willing, him to live. All her tender loving care saved him and they named him Nevada. By the time he was a yearling, Nevada had grown into a big handsome colt and it was decided to leave him as a stallion. Being a Tennessee Walking horse, Nevada had a very smooth rocking-horse gait that was passed on to all of his colts along with his intelligence and calm disposition.

One spring two separate herds of horses were being brought in to be moved to different pastures at dusk. The herd of workhorses, led by a big silver-grey Percheron stallion were to go to the lower pasture. Nevada was leading the riding stock and his herd was to go into the corral.

A shrill piercing challenge split the air as the huge Percheron spotted Nevada. Gloria was trying to get the gate shut, but the enraged horse went right over the top of her as he charged Nevada. Whirling around, Nevada kicked out with his hind feet to block the attacking stallion that out-weighed him by a thousand pounds. Protecting his herd, trumpeting an answering challenge, Nevada lunged at the enraged silver-grey stallion and landed a blow to his withers. The ground thundered and shook. Smaller and quicker, Nevada held his own against his adversary, as he reared, lunged and kicked. Sharp teeth and powerful jaws drew blood as both horses twirled in a circle trying to grab each others jugular vein. Manes flying and tails whipping, the two horses reared up pawing at each other with their front feet. The enraged silver towered above Nevada. All of a sudden, the huge stallion grabbed Nevada's neck and mane in his huge mouth and shook him like a cat shakes a mouse.

Terrified that he was going to kill Nevada, Marie grabbed a fence pole and started hitting the Percheron to make him let go of Nevada. With blood dripping from his mouth, the Percheron swung around to face Marie. Realizing that she was not another stallion, he swung back to get another grip on Nevada's neck. Marie hollered, "Leave him alone!" and clobbered the big stallion again with the pole. Backing off, the big silver-grey came to his senses. Wheeling around, whinnying his triumphant victory scream, he raced back to his herd.

Nevada stood with his head down and one foot raised. Quickly, Lillian caught Nevada and led him limping out of the corral. Since they didn't have a telephone, they couldn't call the veterinarian. They went to town to try and find the vet but had no luck. Finally, after several trips into town searching for him, they talked to the druggist. He told them to put vinegar in a bucket of water and apply wet compresses to Nevada's shoulder that had been gashed open. All night they doctored Nevada. Miraculously, he recovered.

Working with horses was a daily occurrence on the ranch. Gloria was only ten when she opened a gate for a herd of about thirty wild horses to let them through to the watering hole. Before she could get out of the way, the thirsty horses broke into a run. Caught up in the middle, she had to run along with the horses to keep from getting trampled. As the last horse ran past her, she felt lucky to be alive. That was an experience she never wanted to repeat.

Breaking horses to ride was a necessity and Lillian was the most adventurous about riding anything with four legs. Cyclone, a big buckskin, had never been ridden by anyone because he was so wild. Marie said that if Lillian couldn't ride Cyclone, that she would have to send him off to be trained by a bronco buster. Previously, none of their horses had been vicious buckers, they would put their heads down and take a couple of jumps, but they were easy to handle. Cyclone lived up to his name and put on quite a rodeo as he threw Lillian. Nothing hurt but her pride, Lillian agreed with her mom to have someone else train him.

Marie sent him to a cowboy in Polson she felt could train him right. When Clyclone was brought back to the ranch after his training, Marie was very upset because his withers and girth were rubbed raw from an ill-fitting saddle. It took a while for his wounds to heal, but Lillian was able to ride him after that.

Rodeo was a big affair in Polson. Lillian tried out for rodeo queen and everybody in the family, including Marie, sold tickets for the rodeo because the one who sold most, became queen. Lillian won and was presented a beautiful hand-tooled saddle. She rode Nevada in the parade and in the grand entry. Even if he was a stallion, he never bothered any other horses and remained a perfect gentleman.

Always sympathetic towards animals, Marie tangled with a drunken cowboy that was abusing his horse in Polson. Spurring and wheeling his horse around and around, jerking on the bit and beating his horse, the cowboy was showing off to his friends. Marie grabbed the horse's reins and ordered him to get off the horse. Stunned, the cowboy minded and Marie took his horse and tied it up and told his friends to keep him off the horse until he sobered up.

Having been raised to work, work, work, Marie daily rode out to the pastures and checked the horses and cattle. She loved to ride to the top of her mountain and look down over her ranch and Flathead Lake that bordered her property. Carrying a hammer, nails and wire in her saddle bags, she repaired fences every day. Deer, elk and sometimes a wayward cow would go through a fence and leave behind a tangle of wire that had to be sorted, spliced, and tightened.

On one such occasion, she was riding Nevada. Although he was generally very gentle and smart, another stallion, Jim, came running toward them, trumpeting his challenge to fight for his herd. Both stallions, ears back, teeth bared with eyes flashing hatred of each other, reared up. Front feet slashing, and teeth gnashing they lunged at each other.

Terrified, Marie jumped off Nevada's back and started screaming at the two fighting horses.

Blood flecked Jim's shiny white coat as Nevada's hooves found their mark. Reins flapping, Nevada twisted and turned as the white stallion charged time and again. Nevada's raven-black coat was covered with sweat and blood. His saddle loosened and slipped under his belly, hampering his ability to defend himself.

Throwing rocks at Jim and screaming, Marie charged into the conflict, pelting Jim with rocks as fast as she could throw them. Startled, Jim wheeled around and ran off. Trembling, Marie caught Nevada, loosened the cinch, dropped the saddle to the ground from under his belly and quieted him down as she ran her hand over his sweat streaked coat. Resaddling him, Marie rode home, still shaking from the close call.

When Marie was in her sixties, she still rode almost every day. Her favorite horse was Reno, a big buckskin. In a hurry to go one day, she saddled her horse and mounted. Someone had used her saddle and had lengthened the stirrups. Not wanting to take the time to shorten them, she took off for the high country. Tumbleweeds skittered along the ground, rolling end over end, propelled by the strong south wind. Riding along the fence line, Marie saw a piece of tin flapping wildly in the wind. Startled when the tin banged against the fence post, Reno began to gallop. Bouncing in the saddle because her stirrups were too short, Marie wrapped her arms around Reno's neck. Reno flew across the ground as if he were being chased by goblins. Thoughts of landing on the rocky ground raced through Marie's mind. Burying her face in Reno's black mane, she hung on for dear life. Tiring, Reno slowed down and Marie pulled him to a halt. Shaking like a leaf, Marie dismounted and led the horse home, mumbling, "I am too old for this foolishness." That was the last time she rode a horse. From that day forward, she walked everywhere she needed to go.

If she were not going to ride a horse, she had better learn to drive a car. After running into a ditch and ending up in the hospital, she decided that she would never get the hang of controlling an automobile. Getting so excited, she would forget what she was supposed to do, she had several close calls. Finally she gave up trying to learn. After she moved to Polson, she walked the three-and-a-half miles to and from the ranch almost daily. Sometimes a neighbor would see her and give her a lift, but otherwise, she walked.

CHAPTER TWENTY-THREE

WORK AND PLAY

Clasping her arms around her drawn-up knees, perched there on the roof, Marie smiled to herself as she thought about some of the fun times her family had enjoyed. How quickly the years had flown!

Admittedly, she had always been so busy working, that she missed out on many fun activities. The girls doted on Baby Gene. Until he was three months old, Carl would carry him around singing, "Jerusalem, Jerusalem." Marie would sing "Styinkirisy," a song about a Cossack hero who saved their region, and about his wedding troop riding away in a sleigh being chased by wolves – a song, with an up-beat tempo and much too joyous, considering they all perished.

Carl had brought fun into the children's lives, taking them to carnivals, ice skating, and social functions. He bought the first radio in the neighborhood, with a tall free-standing wooden cabinet. The neighbors came from all around to listen to it. Marie welcomed the company as well, and enjoyed visiting and laughing with their friends – every stranger became a friend.

Another diversion was a close neighbor, Alfonse Gucchi, a French Canadian Indian who lived on forty acres just across the road. He liked to drink, and to get the money for liquor, he would go into the woods and bring back firewood. He would get a load ready and take it to town to sell it. Every Saturday he got up early and hitched his ancient horse to his buggy. Riding to town, he tied his horse to the back of a large billboard sign by the bridge, and proceeded to get drunk. Though it was against the law to sell alcohol to an Indian, no one ever told where he got it.

Coming home in the late evening, he would stop at the Johnsons, if he saw a light in the window. Chet would get the horse, take it home, unharness it, and turn it loose in the pasture. Later, he would see that Gucchi got home safely. Sometimes, when Alfonse came home drunk, he would come over carrying his violin and he would play, sing, and dance,

The family in 1938. Gloria is in the front and, from left in the back, are Helen, Marie, Gene, Lillian and Chet.

all at the same time. When he was younger, he had played for dances.

Once in awhile, after being in town, he would walk over with his cane (the younger children imagined it might be a gun) and do his dance to entertain Gene, still a toddler. He would threaten to kill them all except Lillian, because she was dark. He excused Gloria because she brought him over a quart of milk each day. More than one evening ended with Chet putting him to bed.

Gucchi's favorite pastime was sitting at the window of his old house watching the Johnson children. He said there was always some excitement going on and he never knew what to expect. Sometimes it would be Chet and his friends trying to ride a bucking horse. Or a fox might climb over the tall, wire fence, or dig under. Marie would yell to get to the chickens – fast! Chet would get on a horse and try to rope the fox. Pandemonium reigned until the culprit was again back where he belonged.

One time Helen and Gloria had to borrow a tub from a neighbor half a mile away. The horse, Verly, was so tame they could do anything with her. Riding bareback, the two girls had all they could do to stay on and hold the tub, which kept hitting the horse. With each bang the horse galloped faster. According to Gucchi, they made quite an entrance coming into the yard.

Marie often sent him food and no child ever refused to go because he told fascinating stories about the old days. Whenever a horse was killed for fox meat, some was sent to Alfonse. He especially liked groundhog meat.

When Gucchi died, a nephew and his wife moved into the house, but not for long. The nephew died of cancer and Anna, his wife, was found drowned in the creek. Before Anna died, she gave Marie a head scarf to remember her by.

The year after Carl died, Marie borrowed a Santa Claus costume from the Sunny Slope school after the Christmas program, so that Gene could talk to Santa. Lillian wore the suit and had Gene sing a song for her. The next year, there were too many demands for the outfit so Marie brought down an Eskimo suit from the attic and made up a story that Santa got all sooty and had to borrow this suit. Gene kept trying to find Lillian to tell her about Santa, but he looked in vain.

While Marie dedicated her life to operating and expanding the ranch, and paying off debts, the kids were having fun, as kids will. One morning Marie opened the back door and started shrieking. The kids bounded out of bed. Chet and his friends had borrowed a huge wolfhound and left it tied to the kitchen door to trick Marie. It was as large as a small horse and she was frightened for a moment, but then she laughed along with the kids.

One evening Marie sent her girls to bring home the cows. They stopped to play on a wagon wheel, pretending it was a merry-go-round. It was dusk. The cows weren't in to be milked. Marie advanced with a stick...making no attempt to catch them to use it. They had a big supper and went to bed without a spanking. Marie never really punished her children.

Marie went to a great deal of work for birthday parties for the children. They were very simple with no presents, but Marie worked hard cleaning windows and walls, and scrubbing and waxing floors. A special treat served on birthdays was bananas and Jello that was thickened by putting the bowl on the cool basement floor, as they had no refrigerator.

At times Marie brought down her cans of ivory carvings – geese, swans, ducks, sleds, and animals, all beautifully carved. The children were allowed to play carefully with them. They could go through the suitcases of Eskimo parkas, seal skins and different kinds of furs.

One winter she let them use the mukluks to wear over their shoes for warmth. The kids thought they were great for sliding down the highway.

Word got around about Marie's collection. A university professor came to look and to hear about the tribes of people few other people had seen.

When the children were younger, the neighbor children would come to play Annie I Over, Kick the Can, and other games. Most of their neighbors did not have stock, and their children did not have chores to do. But the Johnson children felt like they were helping out and thought life must be boring for the kids who had no horses to ride. Though there was a constant change in the people who came and went, the Johnson children always had friends coming over.

The girls were so close, they called themselves the "Three Musketeers" and did almost everything together. They read movie magazines together and pretended to meet some of the cowboy stars in the movies. Lillian's favorite cowboy was Hopalong Cassidy; Gloria's was Roy Rogers; Helen's was Gene Autry.

The girls enjoyed playing together on the hill above the house, especially in early spring after a long winter. They liked to pick buttercups and other flowers, but especially the delicate purple shooting stars which were quite rare.

One day while picking dandelions and blowing on the bloom to make wishes, Helen, who was seven at the time, wished for a piano. She could not believe her eyes when she saw a pickup with a piano by the house. Marie had arranged to trade pasturing a horse, named Kootenai, for the summer, in exchange for a piano from the Orton Brothers music store in Butte. Helen became so inspired she went on to have a musical career.

Marie had always loved music and encouraged her children in that area. She had brought her balalaika from Siberia and would sing Russian songs to the children. Neighbor children considered it a treat when she would sing for them as well. All the older children had music lessons: Chet, guitar; Lillian, violin; Helen, piano; and Gloria, mandolin. An old-maid school teacher, Miss Siegrist, gave them lessons on an old pipe organ in her cluttered house. She was a kind, dedicated person who only charged twenty-five cents a lesson and usually gave them hot Ovaltine afterward and a huge bouquet of flowers from her garden to take home. She was also their 4-H leader. The children had to walk the three and one-half miles to town for lessons, as they did for Sunday School, choir practice, confirmation class, and Saturday afternoon movies.

There was another activity that delighted the girls. Marie stored boxes of dresses upstairs that had come from Carl's sister, Charlotte Swenson. As the wife of the president of the fur company, she went to quite a number of social affairs. When she was through with the dresses she sent them to Marie. Most of the things were not practical for daily use, especially the high-heeled shoes. The original designers would no doubt have been surprised to see three lively girls, dressed in the sequined, beaded, silk chiffons of the Thirties styles, twirling to the music of the Victrola. On rare occasions, they were permitted to share with the neighbor kids.

Once Charlotte sent a box with dolls – the only ones the girls ever had. Lillian found a large one in the box; Gloria got a very pretty one, but Helen came in late and all that was left was a China doll with a bald head. Marie tried to heal her broken heart by making a joke of it.

"We'll call him Henry," Marie suggested, naming him after one of their eccentric, but good-looking hired men. Henry became quite worn with all the loving he received.

Marie okayed all musical activities for her teenagers. Church doings and public dances at the country club were all right. The girls played in the band so basketball and football games were considered musicals. They would stop for hamburgers on the way home. The mother of one of Gloria's friends would let her daughter go to a special occasion

In a photo taken in the 1970s, Marie is shown on a point of her land overlooking Flathead Lake near Polson, Montana.

if Gloria was going, for Marie's approval meant it would be proper.

Helen was a prom attendant and sang at a lot of school affairs. She went on to sing publicly, performing at school programs, the Showboat, and at Montana State University at Bozeman.

Summertime meant visitors. Charlotte Swenson and her family came to spend their vacation at the ranch. They had money to wear the latest styles and do unusual things, such as bring along a Japanese houseboy, to tend to their personal needs. One year, they brought along their pet monkey. Sometimes they brought the girls clothes, the only new ones the girls got. Marion and Margie, the daughters, were quite sophisticated. Marion was in the forefront of the women's movement, being one of the first to smoke and act independent. She was a great swimmer and swam with the girls out to a big raft they had on the lake.

The Swensons usually rented a place on either the east or west shore of the lake. Charlotte was health-minded, eating honey and keeping goats for milk.

Marion and Margie liked to ride horses with the local cowboys, and, of course, the cowboys were attracted to the beautiful young ladies from the big city. They would ride Marie's horses on the hills above her house. And Marie always gave them all a big farewell picnic.

Marie's obsession for work was the basis of her contempt for men in general, and Carl, specifically. He never worked hard enough, or long enough, to suit Marie. She always had to work harder to do the work she felt he should do. Her expectations were always too high for her children to meet. She loved them, but there was no time to enjoy them – there was too much work to be done.

Always there was a fence to be fixed, weeds to pull, rocks in the road – and nothing but perfection would be acceptable. Once the boys were installing six fence posts. There were six holes within which to place the posts. Critically checking the work, Marie stated, "You put the wrong pole in that hole."

Looking at the job they had done, they couldn't tell the difference between the six fence posts. Pride in their job turned into frustration as they realized no matter which posts they had put in which hole they probably would have been wrong.

As the children began to leave home – Lillian to work in Seattle; Chet to try mining and ranching; Helen and Gloria to college; only Gene remained at home. Gloria felt she should stay at home to help with the cattle and horses, as well as the housework. Marie was adamant. Education was too important. She and eleven-year old Gene would

Marie and the author, Florence Smith, go over a scrapbook of photos during the period the book was being put together.

manage. Besides, Chet lived on a nearby ranch and would help out.

Many a morning, Gene would waken to "Get up! The day is half over already!"

Marie was never interested in remarrying. Many times she made the statement that never again would she take care of a man. She felt Carl had been weak, and she could have done much better with a more ambitious man – someone who desired to acquire more land and work to achieve more.

There was a shoemaker from a neighboring town who made beautiful carvings and a desk for the family. He asked Marie to marry him and was very perturbed when she refused, saying there was no way she could be married and run a ranch, too.

In the late Forties, a widower with grown children became acquainted through cattle trading. He helped Marie with the trucking of her cattle, fixing machinery, and, in general, helping out. Since Marie had been making a go at running the ranch for about ten years, his approach that she couldn't do it by herself was probably the wrong thing to say. He left.

Then there was a plumber who courted Marie. He took her to

shows and for drives. The kids were relieved when she turned him down.

A family friend for many years was interested in marrying Marie. He was a great pianist, but Marie told him, "No." Later, she learned he had a tumor on the brain and was sometimes violent toward those close to him, so she thought it was just as well.

Marie told the children that she could never marry anyone so long as they acted like wild Indians, but, in truth, she enjoyed her independence.

Another widower, whose wife had been crippled for forty-five years before she died, had three grown children. He played the violin. Marie's girls and his daughters tried to promote a romance; they carried a note saying that he wanted to see her. He proposed.

"I have five children; I am too busy; no time to marry," she answered.

He sighed and said, "I guess I will have to take my second choice." And he did.

Looking back, she realized she had compared her feelings toward all men to what she had felt for Nikolai. At 92, she still kept his picture, though she had misplaced the poem.

What would her life have been like if she had been able to return home from Vladivostok? Certainly, she would not have been able to own her own land. Surveying her impressive land holdings, she felt proud of what she had been able to achieve since Carl's death.

And she had been able to return to Russia, but not, of course, to Antipina.

CHAPTER TWENTY-FOUR

TRAVEL AND FAMILY

In 1964, Marie had misgivings about leaving her ranch to accept an invitation to travel. What would she do with her cattle if she went her daughter, Helen McClellan and her husband, Mel, both teachers, who had invited her to go with them to Russia?

It had been twenty years since she had had any contact with her Russian family. Through the Red Cross, she was able to locate a nephew; he wrote her about her sister, Elizabeth and her family. Marie's mother had died in 1928; sister, Barbara, in 1931. Then, sister, Elizabeth wrote to Marie. She said that the cause of Barbara's death was unknown; but of the mother she said, "Mother was condemned, sentenced for reason she sent dispatch. She died a costly death."

The Communists had sent Alexi and Peter to Murmansk when they destroyed the family farm. In 1936, Alexi died in an avalanche while building a road outside of Murmansk. Two other workmen in the slide got out safely, but by the time they got to Alexi, it was too late.

Peter, just a few days after Alexi died, fell from a bridge he was helping build, onto the rocks below. He died two days later.

Alexi's family of five children was located in Leningrad. Their mother was unable to care for them, and the children were scattered. The family had lost track of their brother, Boris, and did not locate him until a notice of a child's birth appeared in the paper, naming Boris as the father.

How Marie longed to go to Russia! But what about the cattle?

A friend told her, "Hang the cattle! Sell them! Put them in a pasture with water and forget them! Of course, you must go!"

So Marie obtained a passport and visa.

Marie sailed from New York on the KUNGSHOLM on July 15, 1964, and joined the McClellans, who had sailed in April, and awaited her in Gothenberg, Sweden. They continued on the train to Stockholm and

Helsinki. Then began a six-weeks tour of Russian sites and cities.

In Moscow, they were delighted to see Marie's sister, Elizabeth, and her daughter, Nina, who had traveled from Tashkent, Uzbakistan, to get there. They brought fruit and an Uzbec hat as gifts.

Marie had always said that she would never get on an airplane, but on her first flight from Moscow to Volgograd (formerly Stalingrad) she sat next to a man who used to live near her home between Tobolsk and Tyumen. She was so interested in what he had to say, she paid no attention to the flight.

Volgograd was called "Hero City." The town was completely destroyed by the Germans during World War II. There are monuments in honor of those who fought house-to-house and hand-to hand-to the last person. Only the remnants of an old building, a granary, remain.

Anna, Marie's next older sister, had lived in Stalingrad. she never learned to read or write, but her daughter, who was a nurse, wrote Marie that German bombs were falling all over – she didn't know whether they would even be alive the next day. Anna and her family of three daughters and one son were never heard from again. Barbara had left all the family pictures, documents, and Marie's diplomas with Anna when she was forced to move from Antipina to Tyumen. All were destroyed in the

Marie astride one of her favorite horses, overlooking Flathead Lake from her land.

bombing.

Wherever they went – Socki, Kiev, and other places, or whatever they did, such as rafting the Dnieper River, Marie was surrounded by people who wanted to talk and ask questions.

At Leningrad (St. Petersburg) Marie had a surprise. Her nephew, Ivan, and a whole room of relatives were there to greet them with flowers. The people on the plane who were most interested in this Russian speaking American, burst out with applause, and curiously and happily watched the reunion.

Relatives had come from all over. Among them, Irina, Alexi's daughter, and her husband had come from Kazan, 1,500 kilometers away, on a motorcycle, with a tent. Ivan, Alexi's son, said the Communist officials would not let Marie, Helen, and Mel visit his home in the little country village of Sableno, 45 kilometers from Leningrad. After much pleading with the officials, Marie and party were allowed to go, but traveling on the train, Ivan warned Marie to be careful what she said.

In spite of two neighbor women who stayed all evening – obviously serving as security guards – Marie had a wonderful evening with Ivan and his wife, Anna. Their home, a little three-room house, had a wood stove, no running water and an outdoor toilet.

Anna was fat and jolly. Her teen-age son, Boris, was there. Anna had twin sons from a previous marriage, one of whom had died of starvation during the siege of Leningrad. She saved one son by scraps she was able to scrounge while working as a nurse.

In addition to Ivan and Irina, they also met two other children of Alexi: Boris was there with his wife, Tamara and daughter, Ludmilla; and niece Marie and her son, Yuri. Sister Liz had also come with daughter, Valla. There were assorted cousins, as well. It was a most joyous occasion.

For six months Marie traveled. Sometimes she took tours on her own, and, at times, meeting with Helen and Mel to visit spots all around the world. They were graciously received wherever they went. Marie was thrilled when their hosts dressed her in native garb, especially in Jerusalem and New Delhi. She tried to do everything, including ride the rapids in the Philippines.

Marie got back in January, 1965, ready to plan the next trip.

Marie's youngest son, Gene, now a counselor for the University of Alaska, Anchorage, wanted his mother to come to see the sled dog races in Alaska. In 1967 she went to Anchorage. To her delight, she learned the son of Pavlov, the Russian teacher at Providenya, who had offered to get her a job, was living in Fairbanks. She and Gene visited him. He had a picture of Marie and Carl in front of their sod cabin at Koluchin Bay; and, though they had not met before, they found a lot in common.

In 1973, Gene and the teacher of Russian Language at the University of Alaska, organized a three-week tour for a group of twenty-seven people, to visit Leningrad, Moscow, Kiev, Tashkent, and Erevan. Marie was a valuable contributor to the group with her ability to speak Russian. She crammed her suitcases as full as she could get them – mostly woolens, for relatives. At the customs where luggage was inspected, she was asked if she had brought gifts.

"Yes, a skirt and blouse." And she definitely had.

She was told she would have to pay their full purchase price as an import tax. The inspector may have suspected there was more, but he accepted the 130 rubles, and let her pass.

Again she had a happy reunion with the Leningrad relatives and her sister, Elizabeth, at Tashkent.

In 1982 she started to refinish old houses; three of them at the ranch, which she rented. She had a good garden at the ranch that year, as well as a good crop of strawberries and raspberries. She sold 30 calves but held the rest; the price was too low. She thought about giving up her

A family gathering.

cattle to travel; she wanted to go to Russia again. She was feeling well and still walked the three and a half miles to the ranch from Polson.

In 1988, she sold all her cattle and went to Russia with Gloria, Helen, and Lillian, just after the Olympics (which the U.S. did not attend.) Again she met with relatives and tried to get Elizabeth to come to the United States. Elizabeth felt it was an impossibility, but said she would fly over with her spirit when she died.

Meanwhile, Marie loved to go to auctions and collect antiques. Her home in Polson was filled with her collections. She always insisted on bargains, to the embarrassment, at times, of her children, who felt it might be appropriate for yard sales, but not for the hardware store. Everything cost "too much."

While money was no longer a factor, the trading skills Papa had instilled in her, always made her feel she must bargain for everything she purchased. Having amassed large land holdings, Marie was quite wealthy, but she never stopped looking for more land bargains, because she did not think she owned enough property yet for her to feel financially secure. Local people had dubbed her the crazy "fox lady," but she had showed them how "crazy, like a fox" she was.

Visits from the family and twelve grandchildren lighten her life and they spend many happy occasions together. Marie became more and more a loner. She did not trust people. Guarding her possessions caused much anxiety.

Having come to terms with her own individuality, her children fondly tease her with her usage of bits and pieces from several languages, creating her own unique expressions, such as: loafmeat – meatloaf, forth and back – back and forth; we go now – let's leave; no monkey-monkey – no monkey business; no playing around – no wasting time.

In December, 1991, a nephew, Boris, with his wife, Irina, came from Russia to visit. They were astonished to find America such a rich country.

Marie comments, "I can remember my old times before the Communists came and part time revolution. We here live like in heaven. I hope it will change in Russia for the best. I never regretted coming to America."

Suddenly fatigue overcame Marie. She did feel better than last year when it was an effort just to cross the street. True, part of it had been her allergic reaction to a cat. The fall of 1990, she had been ill with an enlarged heart and kidney trouble. Not that ill health stopped her. There were weeds and grass in the garden. She laid down to pull them, "I think the ground gives me strength. I feel better now."

Nevertheless, she had to change her heart medication. Oh, well, she supposed old age was creeping up on her.

And as she gingerly felt her way down the ladder, she said, "I have no time to die. I have too much things to finish."

Marie Zimina Johnson.

EPILOGUE

Marie Zimina Johnson died on December 29, 1992, from a heart problem. She had been ailing for some time but her indomitable spirit would not let her succumb. Inconvenienced by failing health, she refused to be handicapped. Determination and a sense of humor served her well as she dictated this story of her life.

As a woman, it never occurred to her to insist on her rights; she took for granted she must earn on her own whatever she got. Circumstances brought out her incredible strength and latent resources. The many small hurts caused by a society that labeled her "crazy" were shrugged off as she laughed when told, "You ARE crazy – like a fox."

Sprinkled on Marie's grave is a tiny bit of soil from her birth land. Her nephew, Boris, returned from Russia, bringing a package of soil and pictures of her old home he had taken on December 28, to fulfill her request, not knowing she had just died and he was too late. Her chaotic and eventful life ended, she is buried in America with a bit of soil from her Russian homeland mingling with soil from a country she grew to love. As a tribute to Marie, the children sprinkled part of the Russian soil on Johnson Point on Flathead Lake, a property that had brought much pride to Marie.

Rest in Peace, my friend.

REFERENCES

Armstrong, T. E. RUSSIAN SETTLEMENT IN THE NORTH, Cambridge University Press, 1965.

Ashton, James M. ICEBOUND, A TRADER'S ADVENTURE IN THE SIBERIAN ARCTIC, G. P. Putnam Sons, New York, 1929.

Capron, Walter Co. Capt. U.S.G.S.,Ret., THE WATTS SEAPOWER LIBRARY, Franklin Watts Inc., New York, 1965.

Chevigny, Hector, RUSSIAN AMERICA, THE GREAT ALASKAN VENTURE, 1741 - 1867, Viking Press, New York, 1965.

Clarkson, Jesse D., A HISTORY OF RUSSIA, Random House, New york, 1961.

Crankshaw, Edward, THE SHADOW OF THE WINTER PALACE RUSSIA'S DRIFT TO THE REVOLUTION, 1825 - 1917, Viking Press, New York, 1967.

Douglas, John Scott and Charles Madsen, ARCTIC TRADER, Dodd, Mead, New York, 1957.

Gleason, Robert J., ICEBOUND IN THE ARCTIC, Alaska Northwest Pub. Co., Anchorage, no date.

Harcave, Sidney, RUSSIA, A HISTORY, 5th Ed., J.B. Lippencort, Philadelphia, 1964.

Hoetzsach, Otto, THE EVOLUTION OF RUSSIA, Harcourt Brace, 1966.

Jenner, Diamond, DAWN IN ARCTIC ALASKA, Jones Press, Inc., U. of Minn., Minneapolis, 1957.

Kapitanoff, Lorraine T., RUSSIAN CULTURE AND CIVILIZATION, Kendall/Hunt, Dubuque, Ia., 1990.

Karpovich, Michael, IMPERIAL RUSSIA, 1801 -1907, Berkshire Studies in European History, Holt Rinehart Winston, 1932.

Kuravov, V., THE TRANS-SIBERIAN EXPRESS, Sphinx Press Inc., New York, 1980.

Levin, M.G. and L.P. Potapav, THE PEOPLE OF SIBERIA, Editors of Chicago Press, Chicago, 1964. Originally published by Russian Academy of Science, Moscow, 1956, under title, NARODY SIBIRI.

Madison, Charles ARCTIC TRADER, 1957.

Massie, Robert K., NICHOLAS AND ALEXANDRA, Atheneum, New York, 1967.

Moscow, Henry, RUSSIA UNDER THE CZARS, A Horizon Caravel Book, American Pub. Co., Harper Row, 1962.
Mowat, Farley, THE SIBERIANS, Bantam Books, New York, 1970.
Newell, Gordon, THE H. W. McCURDY MARINE HISTORY OF THE PACIFIC NORTHWEST, Superior Pub., Seattle, 1966.
Radzinsky, Edvard, THE LAST TSAR, THE LIFE AND DEATH OF NICHOLAS II, (translated from Russian by Marian Schwartz.) Doubleday, New York, 1992.

Rapaport, Stella F., THE BEAR, SHIP OF MANY LIVES, Dodd, Mead, New York, 1962.
Resnick, Abraham, RUSSIA, A HISTORY TO 1917, Children's Press, 1963.
Sale, Robert, SEATTLE, PAST AND PRESENT, University of Washington, Seattle, 1967.
Smolka, H.P., 40,000 AGAINST THE ARCTIC, RUSSIA'S POLAR EMPIRE, William Morrow and Co., New York, 1937.
Sugar, Elizabeth, THE PAGEANT OF RUSSIAN HISTORY, David McKay, New York, 1950.
Swenson, Olaf, NORTHWEST OF THE WORLD: FORTY YEARS TRADING AND HUNTING IN NORTHERN SIBERIA, Dodd Mead, Co., New York, 1944.
Tupper, Harmon and Elsie, TO THE GREATO CEAN; THE TAMING AND THE BUILDING OF THE TRANS-SIBRETIAN RAILWAY, Little, Brown Co., Boston, 1965.
U.S. COAST GUARD ANNUAL REPORT, YEAR ENDING, JUNE l, 1924. Washington Printing Office.
Waxell, Sven, THE AMERICAN EXPEDITION, William Hodge Co., London, 1952. (Translated from Johan Shalberg's Danish version, Vitus Bering's, EAENTYRLIGE OPDAGERFORD, 1733-43)
NATIONAL GEOGRAPHICS:
Chopen, William Wisner, "Glimpses of the Russian Empire," Vol. XXIII, Nov., 1912, Ps. 1043-1078.
Greeley, A.W. Maj. Gen. U.S.A., "The Land of Promise," Vol. XXIII, Nov., 1912, Ps. 1078-1090.
Marsh, Cody, "Glimpses of Siberia, the Russian 'Wild East,'" Vol. XXXVIII, Dec., 1920, Ps. 513-536.
Washburn, Stanley, "Russia from Within," Vol. XXXII, Aug., 1917, Ps. 90-120.
MAPS:
PEOPLES OF THE SOVIET UNION, Nat'l Geog. Society, 1976.
SOVIET UNION TODAY, 1990.